THE GREAT TANK SCANDAL

Frontispiece   This picture, in company with the one which forms the front cover, shows Covenanter tanks of the 4th/7th Dragoon Guards (9th Armoured Division) taking part in an exercise in Britain. The general air of chaos and confusion portrayed seems somehow symptomatic of the unhappy state of British tank production in the early years of the Second World War. Of all the many thousands of tanks produced during that time the Covenanter was undoubtedly one of the worst and the reason for this traffic jam on an otherwise quiet country road may well be that some of them have broken down. By contrast the little Daimler scout car in the foreground was one of the best British AFVs of the era and, in terms of design for a particular role, one of the most effective in the world.

THE GREAT TANK SCANDAL

BRITISH ARMOUR IN THE SECOND WORLD WAR
PART 1

David Fletcher

LONDON HMSO

© Crown Copyright 1989
Applications for reproduction should be made to HMSO
Second impression 1993

ISBN 0 11 290460 2

British Library Cataloguing in Publication Data

A CIP catalogue record for this book is available from the British Library

Front cover: *see frontispiece*

Back cover:
*Churchill tanks abandoned on the
beach at Dieppe after the raid.*

HMSO publications are available from:

HMSO Publications Centre
(Mail, fax and telephone orders only)
PO Box 276, London, SW8 5DT
Telephone orders 071-873 9090
General enquiries 071-873 0011
(queuing system in operation for both numbers)
Fax orders 071-873 8200

HMSO Bookshops
49 High Holborn, London, WC1V 6HB
(counter service only)
071-873 0011 Fax 071-873 8200
258 Broad Street, Birmingham, B1 2HE
021-643 3740 Fax 021-643 6510
33 Wine Street, Bristol, BS1 2BQ
0272 264306 Fax 0272 294515
9-21 Princess Street, Manchester, M60 8AS
061-834 7201 Fax 061-833 0634
16 Arthur Street, Belfast, BT1 4GD
0232 238451 Fax 0232 235401
71 Lothian Road, Edinburgh, EH3 9AZ
031-228 4181 Fax 031-229 2734

HMSO's Accredited Agents
(see Yellow Pages)

and through good booksellers

Contents

Abbreviations

ACV	Armoured Command Vehicle
ADV	Armoured Demolition Vehicle
AEC	Associated Equipment Company
AFV	Armoured fighting vehicle
AMC	Armoured Mine Carriers
AML	Armoured Mine Layer
APC	Armoured Personnel Carrier
ARV	Armoured Recovery Vehicle
BEF	British Expeditionary Force
BPC	British Purchasing Commission
BSA	Birmingham Small Arms
CDL	Canal Defence Light
CIGS	Chief of the Imperial General Staff
CLY	County of London Yeomanry
COW	Coventry Ordnance Works
COXE	Combined Operations Experimental Establishment
DD	Duplex Drive
DNC	Director of Naval Construction
DTD	Department of Tank Design
EBE	Experimental Bridging Establishment
GHQ	General Headquarters
GMC	General Motors Corporation
GS	General Staff
LCT	Tank Landing Craft
LMS	London, Midland and Scottish Railway
LRC	Light Reconnaissance Car
ME	Middle East model
MEE	Mechanisation Experimental Establishment
MFF	Mobile Field Force model
MGO	Master General of Ordnance
MLC	Mechanised Landing Craft

NAAFI	Navy, Army and Air Force Institute
NATO	North Atlantic Treaty Organisation
PWD	Petroleum Warfare Department
RAC	Royal Armoured Corps
RAF	Royal Air Force
RAOC	Royal Army Ordnance Corps
RCAF	Royal Canadian Air Force
RE	Royal Engineers
REME	Royal Electrical and Mechanical Engineers
RTC	Royal Tank Corps
RTR	Royal Tank Regiment
SDF	Sudan Defence Force
SVDC	Special Vehicle Development Committee
TOG	The Old Gang
YMCA	Young Men's Christian Association

Introduction

Over the next five years we will be celebrating, if that is the right word, the fiftieth anniversary of a series of battles, victories and defeats, which together form the historical milestones of the Second World War. Books about those battles already form a massive library, and there are thousands more dealing in every kind of detail with the equipment used to fight them. A relatively small proportion concern themselves with armoured fighting vehicles, mostly tanks, but with only a few exceptions these tend to examine them as machines, in isolation from their environment and human associations. In some small justification for adding even more to the mountain of tomes this book attempts to connect these themes.

British tanks of the Second World War have a frightful reputation, notably when compared with the vaunted German Panzers, and in these chapters I hope to explain, to some extent, how this came to be. If the tank was invented by the British, and first used in action by them, how was it that such an impressive lead was lost in a mere twenty years? The underlying reasons can only be fully appreciated if one takes into account the history of British tank development over that twenty years,* but even this does not explain why, under the stimulus of war, matters did not improve very quickly.

If one looks for scapegoats they might be found in many places – in a government that always skimped on tank development but gave priority to aircraft and warship production, or a War Office that still did not understand the importance of armoured fighting vehicles in modern war, and an industrial regime that could not get its act together. Yet there are extenuating circumstances. British industry, in the late 1930s, had just emerged from a crippling depression. While shaping up to meet a growing world market it was simply not prepared to retool and retrain to pick up penny-packet orders from a military establishment that kept changing its mind. The War Office had a tank policy but it was hamstrung by the Treasury and all too willing to compromise in cases where it should have been insistent. Yet tanks were only a portion of its total commitment. New weapons were required for the infantry and artillery, and new trucks, new uniforms and a host of other things were also needed, from wireless sets and field kitchens to searchlights and medical equipment. For the government, traditionally, the Royal

Navy came first – rightly so for an island nation with extensive dominions – but naval architecture is a time-honoured science in which Britain was a world leader, so there was no risk of muddle or indecision. Aircraft and tanks furnish an interesting contrast. Aeronautics was, comparatively, a brand new discipline, but a very exact one. Its parameters were well understood and most applied equally to civil and military aviation, while its thrilling possibilities attracted the best and most imaginative brains. The tank was of the same generation as the aeroplane but had no civilian counterpart. Its potential attracted few men of genius and it had not developed – rather it became a hole-in-the-wall science, imperfectly understood and many times at the mercy of those who led it into blind alleys. Contemporary reports give the impression that everyone from the First Lord of the Admiralty (Winston Churchill) to the man on the Clapham omnibus saw himself as a tank expert. On past performance Churchill had some justification (few others did), but genuine experts were a rare breed, and when Sir John Carden of Vickers Armstrong was killed in 1935 it was a singular disaster for Britain.

This volume traces the story of British armoured fighting vehicle (AFV) development roughly up to the end of 1942, and it will be followed with a sequel covering the period to the end of the war. Technicalities cannot be avoided, but in an effort to explain why many British tanks were so poor other aspects are given priority. Yet the subject is not just tanks nor exclusively British, and here at least one discovers that it is also not all gloom. Britain built some outstanding AFVs and pioneered the expansion of armour into many specialised roles with a degree of ingenuity that was unmatched elsewhere, but she also relied heavily on overseas aid. The part played by the United States in providing tanks for the British Army is much too great to be overlooked but in the interests of economy of space, and because of limitations of British sources on the subject, this aspect has been kept under tight control and I have not tried to launch into a deep study of American armour. Those countries that formed the British Empire and Commonwealth during the war present a different problem. Their AFV production was much more closely tied to the needs of Great Britain (although this overlapped with local requirements) so the subject has to be covered in a bit more depth. Yet in doing this one is immediately conscious of the fact that most of these nations now have well-informed military-vehicle historians of their own who are better placed to

---

*This subject will be dealt with in a forthcoming book on the inter-war years by the same author.

make a much better job of it than can be done here. Paul Handel in Australia, Bill Gregg in Canada, Jeff Plowman in New Zealand and Richard Cornwell in South Africa are just four among many, invidiously singled out for thanks as – in some cases – unwitting sources of information.

To place the story in its historical context, major events, mostly battles, are used as a backcloth, but I would not wish to pretend that I have treated this side of the subject in any depth, or that anything new is likely to be revealed, Rather, it is hoped that a better grasp of the situation where tank availability, reliability and development are concerned will at least help to explain why certain battles turned out as they did. Sources are largely original –

documents held in the Tank Museum library – but as ever I have relied on many friends who have specialised in particular aspects of the subject. All deserve thanks, but a few names must suffice: Gwyn Evans, Dick Harley, Eric Milam, Mike Taylor and Terry White.

Finally, since it has not been said before, many thanks to my boss at the Tank Museum, Lieutenant Colonel George Forty, for encouraging me to start writing in the first place; may he never urge me to stop! Thanks also Roland Groom, our photographer, for the marathon task of preparing all the prints, and to the staff of HMSO, especially for not reminding me too often that the fiftieth anniversary was getting dangerously close.

1 Scraping the barrel

1 *A Matilda tank dicing with the buses round Marble Arch in 1940. This tank, believed to be* Honiton *of 8th Battalion, Royal Tank Regiment, displays the modified suspension employed on Matildas at this time and it is quite likely that it is powered by the same type of diesel engines that are fitted in these AEC (STL type) double-deckers.*

If nothing else had happened in 1939, if Germany had not invaded Poland and pitched Europe into a Second World War, it would still have been a memorable year for British tank men. On 4 April Army Orders announced that His Majesty King George VI had approved the formation of a Royal Armoured Corps, bringing together eighteen famous cavalry regiments, the eight battalions of the Royal Tank Corps along with its twelve territorial battalions, and twenty-one yeomanry regiments.

It is all too easy to exaggerate the trauma that this amalgamation caused. It was probably more evident in the Officers' Mess after dinner or in the other ranks' wet canteen than in the daily round. After all, these men were professional soldiers; they knew which way the wind was blowing and for the cavalry, mechanisation – if not total conversion to armour – had been taking place steadily since 1928. To the Royal Tank Corps, proud of its hard-won independent status, it seemed like demotion. From being a corps in its own right it was now to be known as the Royal Tank Regiment.

Of course it was the looming threat of war that led to the creation of the Royal Armoured Corps (RAC) in the first place, and it was in the blast-furnace of war that the true tempering took place. This was no time for looking backwards: on the other hand, looking forwards was not calculated to inspire much confidence either. At a generous estimate, the number of armoured fighting vehicles available to be shared between the fifty-nine RAC regiments at the outbreak of war was some 2000 tanks, of which 300 were completely obsolete, while most of the rest were light tanks of very little combat value; around 8000 tracked carriers which, in any case, had to be shared with the infantry; and approximately 200 armoured cars, half of which were between ten and twenty years old.

New machines of all types were on order but it could hardly be called mass production. Contracts were issued to firms with no previous experience of tank building, so initially at least orders were small and production painfully slow. The official establishment of the average armoured regiment was around fifty tanks, and more would be needed for the various training establishments and to form a war reserve. Clearly it was a situation that no one could afford to be complacent about if they understood it – but very few did. The British Army was still a series of compartmentalised regimes commanded by a traditionally inclined hierarchy, and awareness at government level was negligible.

In order to appreciate the state of British tank development in the first year of the war it is first necessary to understand the system employed to control it. There *was* a system, albeit a complicated one, but the impression gained and passed on by many observers was that it functioned with about as much logic as a headless chicken in a farmyard. Before the war, basic tank policy was formulated at the War Office by the Chief of the Imperial General Staff (CIGS) and the relevant heads of departments. Tank – indeed all – military transport design was masterminded in detail by the Directorate of Mechanisation in conjunction with the design department at Woolwich Arsenal or the staff of Vickers-Armstrong. Evaluation of prototypes was carried out by the Mechanisation Experimental Establishment (MEE) at Farnborough and the Royal Tank Corps Gunnery School at Lulworth. Production was the responsibility of the Master General of Ordnance (MGO), while the entire process was governed by the Treasury, which administered the annual vote allocated to tank design and production. In 1934, with rare insight, the renewable Ten Year Plan adopted after the First World War was converted into a Five Year Plan, making 1939 Z Year. Yet until 1937 this vote, for all types of armoured fighting vehicle, rarely exceeded £100,000 per year. This was readily disposed of, but had it not been, any outstanding monies not committed would be forfeit with each new financial year. In 1937, when Italian pretentions in North Africa posed a threat, the annual sum leapt up to £3,500,000; in 1938, year of the Munich Crisis, it went up to £5,500,000, and in 1939 it reached £10,000,000. By comparison, in 1940, when all such restrictions were lifted, actual expenditure was around £200,000,000. The results of this increase were not all beneficial. In 1937 and 1938 the extra money proved, as one commentator put it, like suddenly providing a starving man with more than he could digest. There were simply not enough new designs in the pipeline to absorb the increased funding, so the residue was spent on expanded orders for existing designs. Few of these machines withstood the test of war.

At the end of 1938 the Secretary of State for War, Leslie Hore-Belisha, sought to have the responsibility for design and production removed from his sphere. This was achieved by the formation of a Ministry of Supply under Dr Leslie Burgin, which became operational in the summer of 1939. The object, which was wholly commendable, was to improve the supply situation by injecting into the system a greater degree of drive and business management. Successful businessmen were appointed to senior posts within the new ministry in the hope that their enterprise and initiative would produce better results. Armoured fighting vehicle development was now catered for by a Department of Tank Design (DTD) under the control of a Director of Tanks and Transport, Sir Peter Bennett. Thus, at a crucial time, a gap opened up between the War Office – as representative of the user – and the designers and producers.

The shock caused by events in France a year later, combined with the realisation that this separation was not functioning at all well, led Mr Herbert Morrison, who had replaced Dr Burgin as Minister of Supply in May 1940, to ordain the formation of a Tank Board to act in an advisory capacity and coordinate military and ministerial policy. Under the chairmanship of Sir Alexander Roger of BSA, who had fulfilled a similar role in the Ministry of Munitions in the First World War, the Tank Board comprised a mixed group of representatives from industry and the War Office. The former included Mr Moyses of the Birmingham Railway Carriage Company, AAM Durrant of the London Passenger Transport Board and Mr Thompson representing the Trades Union Council. War Office interests were covered by General Macready and General Pope. Another place on the board was taken by Mr (later Sir) Geoffrey Burton as Director of Tanks and Transport, following the dismissal of Sir Peter Bennett and most of his department in the post-Dunkirk shake up. Durrant's appointment as Director of Design came as something of a surprise, as the post had been expected to go to Dr H E Merritt of David Brown Ltd. Merritt had been serving the Department of Tank Design as an advisor since 1938. His speciality was transmission systems, and his work in this field is discussed in a later chapter.

The Tank Board got off to a vigorous start, holding three meetings in five days in order to settle itself in and come to terms with the immediate problems. This was only a month after the Dunkirk evacuation and the difficulties the board faced seemed insurmountable. British tanks has not done well, and on the basis of his recent experiences in France, Vyvyan Pope argued persuasively for more powerful guns and thicker armour with improved reliability; in other words, a new generation of tanks. But the new Prime Minister, Winston Churchill, demanded increased production of existing types to make up the losses. Bearing in mind his pioneering advocacy of the tank in 1915, Churchill's attitude at this time appears to be inconsistent. While pressing for greater production on the one hand he was promoting rival schemes on the other. The board's terms of reference limited it to advising only when consulted, and it soon began to run out of steam. In October 1940 Sir Andrew Duncan replaced Herbert Morrison at the Ministry and the Tank Board held its last meeting under Roger in the November. Its subsequent inactivity caused Pope to complain bitterly, and it was restructured under Sir James Lithgow early in the new year. Even so, its powers were still inhibited by the desperate situation and it could do little more than concern itself with details. It also evinced a dangerous predilection for compromise which reduced its effectiveness still further, and it rarely met more than once a month.

Before the war tank designs were initiated as General Staff specifications which were then passed to the design department at Woolwich to be translated into detailed drawings and a full-size wooden mock-up. Unless the prototype was to be assembled at the Ordnance Factory no attempt was made to involve the manufacturer until this stage was reached, and the result, inevitably, was compromise. The contractor's ability to build the ideal vehicle depended on the quality and range of his machine tools and the skills of his workforce. These in turn were related to the firm's success as a commercial producer. In the late 1930s the catchphrase was 'business as usual', which in practice meant that only firms without full order books showed any inclination to undertake military contracts. Business was booming in the civilian market and the only firms with production capacity to spare were those unable to get their share. John Fowler and Co of Leeds, the Vulcan Foundry at Newton-le-Willows – with Harland and Wolff of Belfast the prescribed exception – were among the firms in this unhappy position, so they got the main contracts.

It was largely their adherence to traditional practices that got them into this position in the first place. They lacked modern plant, the skills required to develop new techniques and the resources to acquire those skills. As an example, an experimental department at Woolwich had evolved a satisfactory method of welding armour-plate in 1934 which should have revolutionised tank production in Britain. But the firms already mentioned were, respectively, agricultural engineers, locomotive manufacturers and shipbuilders. Their plant and skilled workforce were all geared to traditional riveting techniques and the tanks they built reflected this. They were also proud exponents of the great British art of craftsmanship. One author has defined craftsmanship as 'the ability to fit together two things that do not fit' and, revered as this tradition may be, it hardly suits mass production; nor did it augur well for the interchangeability of parts when they had to be transferred in a hurry, in the field. In both Germany and Russia, where weapons production was carried on with the fervour of a crusade, the welding of armour plate had been practised for years before the war and both countries soon established a commanding lead in the technique. In the United States mass production demanded a degree of standardisation in which craftsmanship had no place. Automated machine-tools ensured that parts fitted precisely, without modification. Any item that did not meet this standard was immediately rejected.

In Britain there were two exceptions to the general trend, although both remained traditionalists at heart. Vickers-Armstrong had already established a considerable reputation as tank builders which entitled them, in their own view, to virtual independence. Their design team worked directly, if somewhat loosely, from General Staff specifications basing the projected tank firmly on the known capabilities of their plant. This gave them an enviable degree of leeway to build what they liked, although in fairness it has to be said that they did their utmost to give the army what it wanted. They also, at least until war broke out, had a healthy export trade which reduced

their dependence on War Office orders. The other company was Nuffield Mechanisation and Aero, founded by William Morris (Lord Nuffield) in 1937 as the weapons branch of his automotive empire. A new factory was built in Birmingham on modern flow-production lines where a tank could be entirely assembled under one roof. Yet the nucleus of its design and production staff was drawn from a sister company, Morris Commercial Motors, which at that time produced nothing larger than an 8-ton lorry.

The state of Britain's commercial-vehicle industry before the war also had a direct bearing on tank design. The factors that influenced it were many, but there were two major ones. The first was the comprehensive railway network which continued to dominate long-distance movement of freight, especially the heavier bulk materials. Secondly – and to some extent in deference to the railways – government taxation, as defined in the Road Traffic Act of 1930, severely penalised hauliers operating vehicles with a payload that exceeded 2½ tons. As a result, mainstream development was directed towards the production of relatively light-weight lorries that did not require large, powerful engines. At the same time actual tank production was on such a pathetic scale that very few companies were inspired to invest anything at all in the development of more powerful units.

For a few months after the outbreak of the First World War the British motor industry was seriously embarrassed by an almost total dependence on German-made magnetos, the supply of which immediately dried up. By 1939 Britain was self-sufficient in many of the items needed for the construction of military vehicles. Those essential imported items such as rubber, manganese and nickel, which came from sources within the Empire, were never seriously compromised. The problem was more one of manufacturing capacity: there were not, for instance, enough steel mills and foundries to maintain adequate supplies of armour plate. Thus early in 1939 some 14mm armour for the A9 cruiser tank was ordered from Böhler & Co, in Nazi-occupied Austria. The quality of the plate on delivery was found to be on a par with a good British armour, which must have been useful information, but the reverse factor was that it gave a potential enemy a very good idea of the current armour standard of British tanks. The shortage of available factory space for the construction of complete tanks also gave rise to the 'parent' system of manufacture. Contracts were issued to a variety of firms working under the supervision, or parentage, of a nominated company which had been involved in the project from the earliest stage. The task of these subsidiary firms was something more than that of sub-contractors who only undertook to produce specific parts. They carried out the construction of major subassemblies, and often built complete tanks. The former, however, led to a highly inefficient system in which large pieces of tank, like hulls or turrets, were being carted to and fro across the country before final assembly could take place. This not only wasted time and resources, it sometimes led to examples of inferior stock being produced.

When war was declared in September 1939, seven or eight different models of tank were in production for the British Army, four or five more existed in prototype form or advanced stages of design, while others were only undeveloped paper-projects. This variety has led some to conclude either that tank policy was in total disarray, or that no policy existed at all. The fact is that, apart from a few examples, most tanks were being produced to a considered theme, based on specific theories. The trouble was that these ideas had only been formulated within the previous five years: they remained untested while the tanks that would embody them were being built.

In essence the concept was of a range of tanks to fulfil the various functions perceived for armour on the battlefield. At the forefront, in terms of tactical thinking if not design, were the light tanks intended as reconnaissance machines for the mechanised cavalry. They were three-man tanks armed with a pair of machine guns and equipped with wireless, and were lightly armoured, relying on their speed, small size and manoeuvrability to stay out of trouble when on scouting missions. Next in line came the cruiser tanks, which were seen as the main offensive mobile fighting element, initially sub-divided into two groups. The basic cruiser was again primarily a cavalry tank, backing up the light recce tanks and exploiting any weakness in the enemy positions to achieve a breakthrough. It carried a high velocity 2-pounder (40mm) gun capable of penetrating the armour of most foreign contemporaries although its own armour protection was no more than 14mm thick. Thus it too relied on its speed to avoid confrontation unless absolutely necessary, in favour of wide outflanking movements. The cruiser tanks formed the mobile striking force that had first been promulgated in Fuller's famous Plan 1919. In action the intention was to back them up with battlecruiser tanks, armoured to a 30mm standard but carrying the same armament. A change of policy in 1939 attempted to combine the qualities of these two groups with an increase of armour standard for all cruisers and, when this was applied, the battlecruiser concept died at the prototype stage. Infantry tanks formed the final group. These were slow, heavily armoured machines capable of absorbing considerable punishment while they kept pace with the foot soldier during frontal attacks on defended objectives. They were designed to carry between 60mm and 80mm of frontal armour and mount a heavy machine-gun or 2-pounder at a top speed of no more than 15 mph. Since it was believed that fighting in Europe would take the form of frontal assaults on consolidated positions, this type of tank was initially favoured at the expense of cruisers, which were seen as more suited to the open style of warfare encountered in desert regions. As a consequence production in Britain gave highest priority to the infantry

tank programme.

If the theories that dominated tank design were as yet relatively unformed, they were certainly not the only influential factors. There were also a number of externally imposed limitations which had to be taken into account. These included the load-bearing capacity of standard military bridges and the railway loading gauge. The importance of this should not be under-estimated. Since lorry-type tank transporters only existed in prototype form before the war, the long distance movement of tanks in Britain and on the Continent was normally carried out by rail. Factories and docks were all rail served, while branch lines ran into most of the significant military establishments in the country. The loading gauge was a set limit on height, width and shape for all items carried by rail: height because of overbridges and gantries; width to clear platforms, signal posts and other trains; and shape to avoid fouling the arched upper section of tunnels. All these dimensions affected tank design but the greatest of all was width. There are few empirical ratios in tank engineering but the one that associates length with width is vital. Within fairly broad limitations a tank must get wider as it gets longer or it will be impossible to steer on its tracks. Since the width of a tank's hull also limits the diameter of its turret ring it follows that this measurement also controls the size of gun that can be mounted in it. Thus, while they were building tanks which adhered to these restrictions, British designers were in a sense held in check by parameters laid down around a century before by the civil engineers who first created the railway system. Although the weight factor was already controlled to some extent by shortage of suitably powerful engines, this was compounded by the load-bearing capacity of portable military bridges. Before the war this had been set at 16 tons, although the Experimental Bridging Establishment at Christchurch had recently developed a small box-girder bridge which would accept heavier loads, over a much shorter span.

British doctrine conceived the tank primarily as a weapon for fighting other tanks. To this end all models except the light reconnaissance machines and the first infantry tank had to carry a gun capable of defeating enemy armour, to the virtual exclusion of anything else. The weapon chosen was the quick-firing 2-pounder, which first appeared as a towed anti-tank gun in 1936. It was a superb piece of equipment capable of penetrating 40mm of armour at ranges up to 1000 yards. Its semi-automatic breech permitted a high rate of fire and the small rounds were easy both to stow and handle. Unfortunately, due to circumstances that are explained later, it remained the only effective anti-tank weapon in service until 1942, by which time it equipped all eight types of gun tank in British service. Without its gun a tank is useless, and one of the important features of progressive tank design is that each new model should mount a better weapon than its predecessor. Britain failed to appreciate this for far too long. Throughout the inter-war years War Office policy required tanks to be able to fire accurately on the move. With the medium tanks of that period, equipped with geared elevation and manual traverse, crews achieved a skill at this which was the envy of their rivals. With the advent of the cruiser tank British designers pioneered a form of hydraulic power traverse but, at the same time, with the introduction of the 2-pounder mounting they reverted to a system of free elevation. Power traverse demanded a well-balanced turret; free elevation required a well-balanced gun. To obtain the former the usual practice was to mount the wireless set in the back of the turret where it acted as a counterbalance, but in order to balance the gun it was essential to fit it in such a way that a good deal of the overall length was housed inside the turret. These two features meant that the average British tank turret was very cramped, and conditions were not improved by the other practice, regarded as essential by the Royal Tank Corps, of insisting on a minimum turret crew of three men.

The 2-pounder gun fired a solid shot for penetrating armour and a high-explosive round which held such a small charge that it was virtually useless and rarely carried in tanks. A high-explosive shell is the best means a tank has of dealing with what are called soft targets – motor transport, groups of men in the open or machine-gun positions. It is also the best way of knocking out anti-tank guns. Without such a round a tank has to rely on its machine guns, and although these are just as effective in dealing with most of these targets, the anti-tank gun usually has a small armoured shield to protect its crew. It also invariably out-ranges a machine gun, so it can knock out the offending tank before the latter has a chance to reply. The only alternative weapon available at the outbreak of war was a 3.7-inch breech loading mortar which was soon replaced by a 3-inch howitzer, but they both had such a short range that the high-explosive shell could rarely be used effectively, and the main purpose of the weapon was to fire a smoke shell to mask the tanks from enemy fire. Tanks thus armed were known as close-support tanks and they were issued, in small numbers only, to headquarters squadrons of armoured regiments. The logic of providing even a few tanks whose sole purpose was to fire smoke shells almost defies explanation. Not only was it invariably impossible to ensure that they would be where they were most needed at the right time; it was also obvious that if they did unintentionally find themselves matched against an enemy gun-tank they were defenceless.

Most British tanks mounted two machine guns, one coaxially with the main armament so that it shared the same elevation and traverse, the other in the front of the hull. The War Office seems to have been obsessed with the idea that these hull-mounted weapons should have the widest field of fire possible, and often went to extraordinary lengths to achieve it. The most extravagant example was the A9 Cruiser which actually had two hull machine-guns, each in a separate little turret, which could cover an arc of about 120° on either side. This was an extreme case, based on pre-war concepts, but the era of the sub-turret was still not quite over, and it stayed to spoil the lines of many a new tank without adding anything worthwhile to its offensive powers.

By 1939 most industrialised nations had established a tank-building industry and in almost every case it was possible for an observer to recognise certain national characteristics in each country's designs. This was most noticeable in the area of suspension and tracks, which inevitably became important features in tank recognition. It also indicated an element of standardisation, which allowed a degree of interchangeability with a consequent economy in the provision of spare parts. It applied almost everywhere except Britain where, it seemed, each new model appeared with a completely new arrangement. Vickers-Armstrong did achieve a degree of standardisation with their light tanks up to Mark VI, but the next model was completely different. Their cruisers, A9 and A10, shared Carden's 'bright idea' suspension with the Valentine but the first of the Nuffield cruisers, the A13, employed the American Christie system, which did, however, remain in use until the end of the war. The worst examples were the infantry tanks. The Mark I used an old Vickers leaf-spring arrangement while the Mark II, Matilda, was designed around the so-called 'Japanese' suspension. The Churchill was different again, with a multiplicity of small, individually-sprung rollers. Within their limitations most of these systems worked well enough, but from the supply point of view they created a nightmare, and what they appear to say about the harmony of British tank design is their most significant factor.

Numerically the most important type of tank in service when war was declared was the Light Mark VI. Earlier models, some dating back to 1931, were still used (mainly for training), and as a fighting machine the Mark VI was not much of an improvement. It was armoured to a maximum of 14mm, which would resist rifle and machine-gun bullets – otherwise, it relied on a top speed of 35 mph to keep out of trouble. It carried a crew of three – driver, gunner and commander (who also operated the radio). It mounted a pair of machine guns, the excellent .303 inch water-cooled Vickers and its much less reliable .5 inch cousin. The coil spring suspension was both tough and reliable and it ran on good quality, long-lasting tracks, but it was short in relation to its width and pitched violently on rough ground, which made accurate gunnery impossible. The light tank was built by a variety of firms under the parentage of Vickers-Armstrong and appeared in four versions, Marks VI, VIA, VIB and VIC. It was the VIB that bore the brunt of the action along with the much less common VIC, which was an unplanned addition to the family. Shortly before the war a decision had been taken to replace the water-cooled Vickers guns with an air-cooled

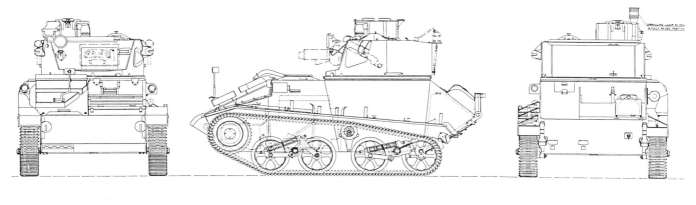

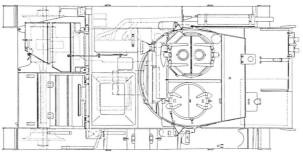

Drawing A: Light Tank Mark VI.

weapon, the Besa, which had been developed from a Czechoslovakian design. The standard model was of 7.92mm calibre but the light tank also mounted a larger 15mm version in place of the .5 inch Vickers.

The first of the cruiser tanks was the A9, or Cruiser Mark I, although it had only carried that designation since 1938. When first conceived in 1934 it was intended as a medium tank suitable for employment with the Tank Brigade, but its actual role – as cruiser or medium – was the same. Built in small numbers by Vickers-Armstrong and Harland and Wolff it was soon downgraded to the status of an interim design. As such, it was a mish-mash of outmoded and modern features. The best of these were the Carden suspension and reliable AEC engine; the most archaic, the pair of auxiliary machine-gun turrets already mentioned. These not only created a series of lethal shot-traps in the angles they formed with the rest of the hull, but also made it impossible to even consider up-armouring when the 14mm plate proved to be too thin to resist enemy shot. A9 carried a crew of six; driver, gunner, loader, commander and, of course, the two machine-gunners. The main turret carried a coaxial mounting for a 2-pounder and Vickers machine-gun, or a 3-inch mortar in the close-support version.

Designed originally as a more heavily armoured medium tank for infantry support – to work with Army Tank Brigades – the A10 was redesignated Cruiser Mark II in 1938. It shared the A9's suspension, engine and simple clutch and brake transmission but was better armoured, with a maximum thickness of 30mm. Yet this

was only achieved by the dubious practice of bolting an extra layer of plate over the basic hull panels; composite armour of this sort was generally considered less effective than single plates of the full thickness. As first built the tank had a well-sloped hull without any auxiliary machine-guns, but the demand for at least one caused a redesign

2 *Testing an A9 cruiser tank over a trench provides a good view of the flexibility of Carden's so-called 'bright idea' suspension design. Actually this approach to trench crossing would be an excellent way of ripping the tracks off a tank. The picture shows clearly the two front machine-gun turrets but, it should be noted, the main turret armament has not yet been fitted.*

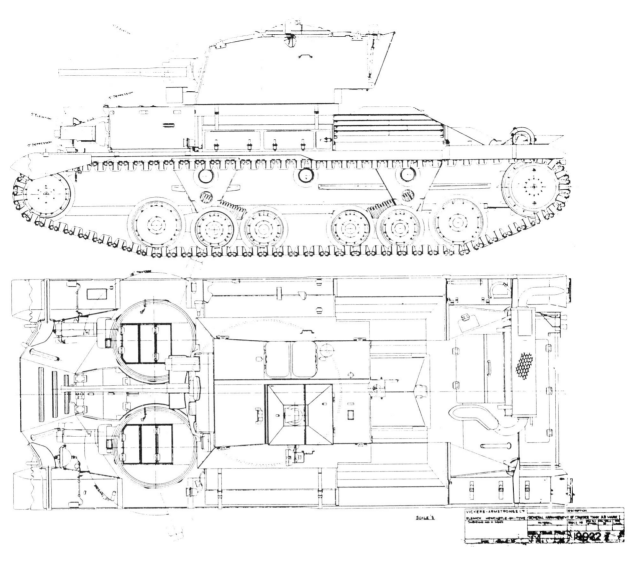

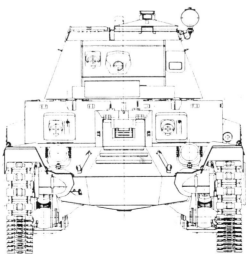

Drawing B: The A9, or Cruiser Tank Mark I.

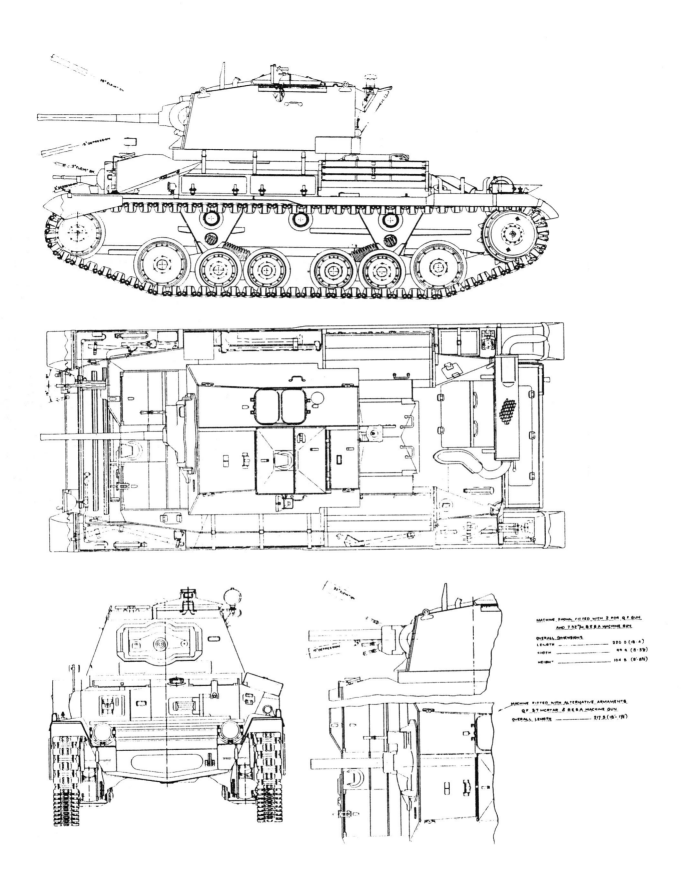

Drawing C: The A10, or Cruiser Tank Mark II showing, in addition, the Close Support version.

3 *A10 cruiser tanks nearing completion at the Birmingham Railway Carriage & Wagon Co., factory. Notice that the two tanks at the far end have a different type of gun mounting.*

at the prototype stage, with the result that the front of the tank presented a broad vertical face to an attacker. The general change from Vickers to Besa machine-guns caught A10 in midstream. Thus in theory at least the original model, the Cruiser Mark II, carried a 2-pounder and coaxial Vickers in the turret with a Besa in the hull front. In practice the hull gun was eliminated on this model since it would only have confused ammunition supply. A later version with Besas in both mountings entered service as the Mark IIA. Again, as an interim design, A10 only appeared in relatively small numbers from Vickers-Armstrong and two or three other firms. The last of these, A W Crabtree & Co, only built ten from an order for 100 – they experienced production difficulties, especially when asked to consider fitting their tanks with a diesel version of the AEC engine instead of the regular petrol model. Like A9 there was also a close-support version of A10.

One of the results of a meeting on future tank policy held shortly after the end of the First World War was an agreement to monitor tank design in other countries. It is clear that this was never pursued very conscientiously, since Britain's first knowledge of the successful American Christie suspension system resulted from a visit by two senior army officers to the Russian manoeuvres of 1936. In fact the system had been available since 1928 and had been heavily publicised as often as its inventor could arrange it, but so far only the Soviet Union had shown any serious interest. It was the decision to adopt this form of suspension in Britain that led to the premature relegation of the A9 and A10 tanks in favour of a new model to be designated A13, or Cruiser Mark III. It was built by Nuffield Mechanisation and Aero and carried a turret similar to the A9 pattern – although it was fitted with a drum-shaped cupola for the commander – and the same armament. Armour was again to the 14mm standard but it was supposed that with a top speed of 30 mph it would be a hard target to hit. The highly flexible nature

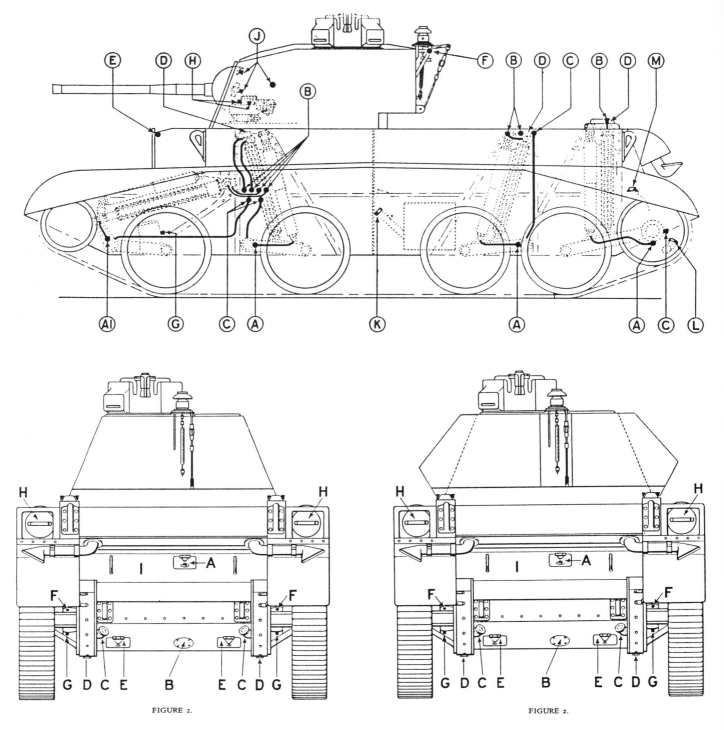

FIGURE 2.   FIGURE 2.

A. Access door over gearbox filler cap, tail-light junction box, and inspection lamp socket.
B. Access plate under gearbox drain plug.
C. Final drive filler caps.
D. Final drive drain plugs.
E. Access doors under brakes.
F. Greasers for rear axle arm pivot bearing.
G. Greasers for rear shock absorber bottom eyes.
H. Air cleaner handles.
I. Rear sloping plate over transmission compartment.

A. Access door over gearbox filler cap, tail-light junction box, and inspection lamp socket.
B. Access plate under gearbox drain plug.
C. Final drive filler caps.
D. Final drive drain plugs.
E. Access doors under brakes.
F. Greasers for rear axle arm pivot bearing.
G. Greasers for rear shock absorber bottom eyes.
H. Air cleaner handles.
I. Rear sloping plate over transmission compartment.

Drawing D: The A13, or Cruiser Tank Mark III. The side elevation shows the layout of the Christie suspension while the two rear views compare the turret outline of the Mark III (left) with the up-armoured Mark IV version (right).

of the Christie suspension demanded a considerable clearance beneath the track guards but the method of construction, whereby the springs were sandwiched between inner and outer hull plates, was designed to improve protection in this area. The rest of the hull took the form of an oblong box, stepped at the front with a protruding headcover for the driver, but there was no provision for a hull machine-gun. In order to produce sufficient power for the tank, in the absence of anything suitable from the British motor industry, Nuffields chose a modified version of the First World War Liberty aero engine from the United States. This 340hp V12 had first been used in the Mark VIII heavy tank of 1918, but by 1939 it left a lot to be desired in terms of reliability. An initial order for sixty-five A13s was on the point of completion when a new General Staff specification was issued requiring a 30mm armour basis for all cruiser tanks.

Attempts to uparmour the A13 resulted in the Cruiser Mark IV, which was basically the same tank with extra panels of armour bolted on. These were fixed directly to the hull, but on the turret they were spaced a few inches away from the original structure and sharply angled to give the turret a diamond-shaped outline when seen from the front. A 30mm mounting was also specified for the armament, but in the event some tanks left the factory with the old 14mm pattern until supplies were used up. Additional armour of the same type was retrospectively fitted to some of the original A13s, which made them difficult to distinguish from the new version. This added about one ton to the overall weight, bringing it up to 15 tons, but this does not appear to have affected its performance. An even later version (the Mark IVA) appeared, in which Besa replaced the coaxial Vickers gun; the tanks were otherwise identical. Over 200 were built by Nuffields and a further sixty-five came from the London Midland and Scottish Railway (LMS) works at Crewe.

The A11, or Infantry Tank Mark I, was the only machine of this type actually in service when the war broke out, but since the War Office never ordered more than 140 of them it was not exactly common. This was just as well: the A11 had been built down to a price, and when price becomes the principal feature in a tank's design that tank is obviously not going to amount to much. In fact it had two things going for it, thick (60mm) frontal armour and a reliable Ford V8 engine. On the debit side, the tracks and suspension were dangerously exposed, the crew of two inadequate and the armament pitiful. The tiny turret was designed to house a single .303 Vickers gun, although the .5 inch version could be substituted, but neither had any worthwhile anti-tank capability. Seen as a well-protected, mobile machine-gun post it was adequate, but as a tank it was a travesty. When obliged to behave as a tank it was handicapped by a miserable top speed of 8 mph and was unable to do more than chip paint off enemy machines, despite the fact that it was invulnerable to their guns. The driver's duties were simple

enough but the other crewman was not only expected to function as commander, gunner and loader of the Vickers gun, he was also the wireless operator. Since there was no room in the turret for the wireless set it was located down in the hull, and in order to work it the commander had to squat down on the floor; all the while he was doing this the tank was not only blind but quite unable to fight.

Only a couple of examples of the Infantry Tank Mark II had been issued when war was declared and delivery was slow. Known officially as A12, but universally as Matilda, it was constructed from a series of large castings bolted together, which gave great strength but demanded an inordinate amount of specialist skills in its manufacture. With a maximum frontal armour thickness of 78mm it was the most heavily armoured tank in existence at the time, and even its suspension was fully protected by 25mm thick skirting plates. Six companies, under the parentage of the Vulcan Foundry, were responsible for construction, but due to the slow pace of work many of the 3000 or so tanks built were obsolete even before they entered service. At 26 tons Matilda was a good deal heavier than most of its contemporaries but reasonably mobile at 15mph. Naturally no suitable engine was available to push this sort of weight around so the tank was designed to take a pair of AEC, and later Leyland, diesel engines of the type used in London buses, and this complication increased the time required for maintenance. Matilda was the first type of British tank powered by diesel engines to enter service. The War Office had expressed a preference for the type, not for mechanical reasons but simply because diesel fuel was less inflammable than petrol. The latter, they commented, was only acceptable if the fuel was well protected, but actually the majority of tanks used by the Royal Armoured Corps for the rest of the war employed petrol engines, and no extra efforts were made to render them fireproof. All the tanks so far described had fairly simple transmission and steering systems. More complex designs were under development but at this stage most designers preferred to use ordinary four-speed commercial gearboxes with clutch and brake steering although this was very wasteful of power. In Matilda things became a little more sophisticated, with the adoption of a Wilson six-speed preselector gearbox and Rackham steering clutches, but the effect was much the same. Inevitably the A12 was armed with a 2-pounder, although a few of the wasteful close-support types appeared mounting a 3-inch howitzer. There was no provision for a hull machine-gun after a scheme to fit an auxiliary turret was rejected at the design stage, and the coaxial weapon followed the usual pattern, a water-cooled Vickers in the Mark I and the Besa in subsequent versions. These tanks also carried a crew of four.

From the early days of the First World War through to the 1930s the British were inveterate advocates of the armoured car. But when the light tanks appeared in the early thirties it was considered that the era of the armoured

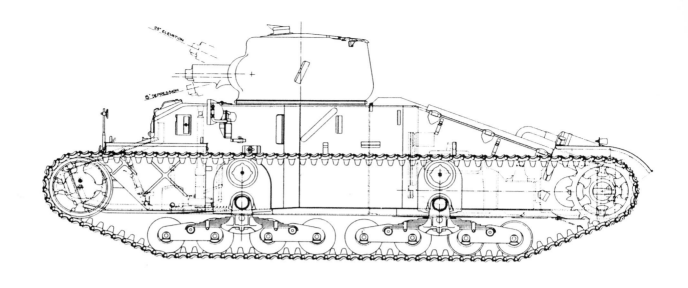

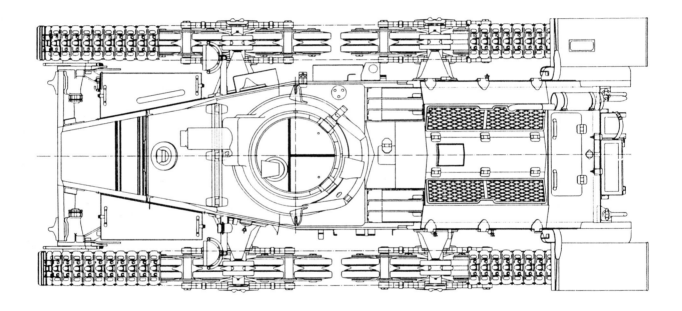

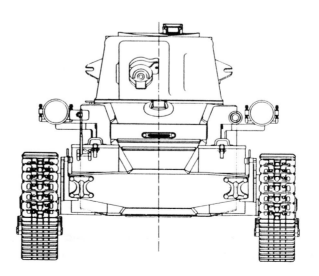

Drawing E:
The A11, or Infantry Tank Mark I.

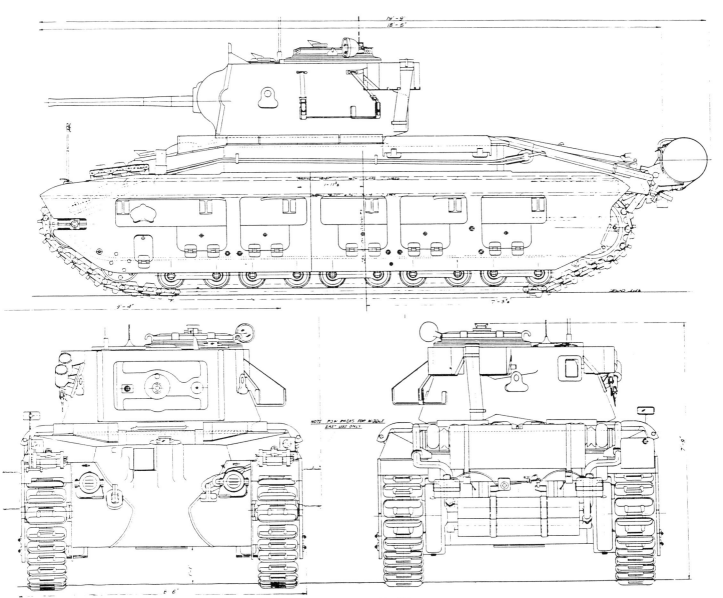

Drawing F: The A12, or Infantry Tank Mark II, better known as Matilda.

car was over. Light tanks had a reasonable top speed, durable tracks and a much better cross-country performance than wheeled vehicles. They were noisier, of course, and demanded a lot more attention in terms of maintenance, but it was clear from the large number ordered that they were seen as the ideal reconnaissance machine for a tank army. If there was still a need for armoured cars they should according to the War Office be long-range scouting vehicles with only modest protection and armament. Most of their work would be confined to the roads so there would be no need for complications such as four-wheel drive and, in due course, the authorities settled for 100 Morris CS9 armoured reconnaissance cars, fifteen of which were ultimately completed as armoured command vehicles. The recce cars had an uninspired design with a high box-body and shallow open-topped turret. They carried a crew of four, and the armament consisted of a Bren gun, Boys anti-tank rifle and smoke-grenade discharger. They had a respectable top speed of 45 mph but their armour was only 7mm thick, making them vulnerable to almost anything more powerful than a pistol.

The essence of reconnaissance is stealth. Its object should be to acquire information speedily without having to fight for it and make a clean getaway, to report as quickly as possible. The ideal vehicle for this role should be fast, inconspicuous and highly mobile in all conditions. British attempts to fulfil these criteria were, unquestionably, very effective indeed. They resulted in the appearance of the Daimler Scout Car, developed from a BSA design of 1938. Scout cars of this type were exclusive to British and Commonwealth armies for most of the war and, indeed, no other nation made a serious effort to emulate them. The Daimler was a highly specialised vehicle which, apart from its engine, owed little to commercial-vehicle practice at all. It carried a crew of two in a low, pot-shaped hull of welded construction in plate up to 30mm thick. The engine was at the rear and the transmission incorporated a Daimler fluid flywheel and preselector five-speed gearbox coupled to a separate forward and reverse selector. Thus it was possible to drive the car with equal facility in either direction, which was suited to rapid disengagement when required. Early models featured four-wheel steering in addition to four-wheel drive, but this proved to be more trouble than it was worth. A Bren gun was carried for emergency use but in practice the cars relied on their top speed – up to 55 mph – and superb agility to keep out of trouble.

Just before the war opinions on the respective merits of light tanks and armoured cars seemed to undergo a change. This was prompted as much by the usual desire for economy as anything else since tanks of any kind were expensive to produce. As if to emphasise the point the term 'wheeled tank' was coined to describe a new type of turreted, fully armoured, four-wheel drive vehicle carrying two machine-guns. Their appearance stemmed from the development of short wheelbase four-wheel drive artillery-tractors called Quads, which were being produced by Guy, Karrier and Morris-Commercial Motors. Special rear-engined chassis of each type were evaluated for armoured car work and Guy Motors of Wolverhampton was chosen to start production. The body was built to a design worked out at Woolwich and, following tests of the pilot models, 100 were ordered. The pilot hulls had all been of riveted construction but it was suggested that welding might be more suitable for the service models. Quite where this idea came from is not clear. The Guy company claimed the credit for themselves but there is good reason to suspect that a certain amount of coercion was involved, bearing in mind popular opinion against it

at the time. It was a much more dramatic step than is sometimes realised because a welder, working on a complex object like an armoured hull, would have to contort himself into the most uncomfortable poses to reach some of the nooks and crannies. The company therefore worked out the design for a rotary jig which could hold the entire body and turn it in such a way that the welder could work on it in comfort. Development of this jig earned the company an important award in due course. The armour on these vehicles was 15mm thick but the plate proved to be so brittle that often a loud noise in the factory, like a spanner hitting the floor, was enough to crack or shatter it as it stood in the racks. In view of this, doubt was expressed about its potential behaviour under fire, but it seems that once the hulls were assembled the problem disappeared. The Guy appeared in two forms; the first fifty were completed with two Vickers guns, like the light tanks, but the second batch carried Besas, and the designation Mark IA. they took a crew of three and had a top speed of 40 mph with a weight of just over 5 tons, but they were not popular in service because they proved unreliable. The makers blamed this on a War Office decision to fit larger wheels and tyres than originally specified but evidence suggests that there was more to it than that.

The term Bren Gun Carrier has been used to describe a whole family of light tracked vehicles designed by Vickers-Armstrong. They were simple, open-topped machines with a lightly armoured (10mm) crew compartment at the front and a standard Ford V8 engine and transmission at the back. Their most interesting feature was the steering system, which caused the tracks to curve when taking large radius bends but applied brakes in the normal way for sharper turns. The true Bren Carrier was issued to infantry battalions and soon proved immensely popular for all kinds of work. It carried a crew of three with the driver and gunner at the front and the weapon protruding

4   A Daimler scout car Mark I in the markings of 2nd Armoured Division showing the armoured roof and steering linkage to the rear wheels.

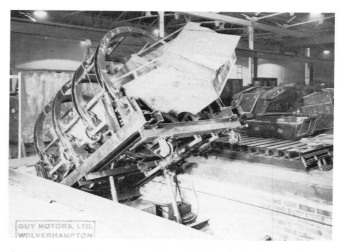

5   The hull of a Guy armoured car held firmly in the special welding manipulator at the Guy Motors factory in Wolverhampton.

6 *A14E1, the LMS heavy cruiser, on a Scammell tank-transporter. The main turret is reversed but the only weapon fitted is the* smoke bomb discharger.

through a slot. Although this permitted the gun to be fired from within the vehicle the object, in theory, was to use it dismounted, since accurate fire was almost impossible on the move.

Another, virtually identical, machine was the Scout Carrier, which was issued to mechanised cavalry regiments for use in company with their light tanks. It mounted a Boys rifle at the front with a Bren gun, on an anti-aircraft mounting, in the rear compartment. This section was enlarged, in comparison with the Bren Carrier, to provide room for a No 11 wireless set operated by the third crewman. The other version was the Cavalry Carrier, which had seats along the sides providing room for six men and stowage for their rifles. It was designed to transport cavalrymen, who it protected from nothing but the weather, but allowed them to dismount swiftly for action. The object was to operate these carriers in conjunction with tanks, but the advent of the armoured division eliminated this role and production ceased after only fifty had been built. Modified carriers were also issued to the Royal Artillery as forward observation-post vehicles, the main difference being the deletion of the weapon aperture. Attempts were also made to develop an anti-tank carrier,

mounting the 2-pounder gun, although this never proceeded beyond the prototype stage. Like the scout cars these little carriers were a uniquely British design and saw service only in limited numbers with foreign armies, but they were used in their thousands by British and Commonwealth forces until the end of the war and beyond, although they had undergone a number of changes by then.

The armoured vehicles just detailed all saw service with the British Expeditionary Force (BEF). Newer models were in the pipeline while others never developed beyond the prototype stage. Among these were the heavy battle-cruiser tanks like A14, a sort of modernised A7 Medium built by the LMS, and A16, a big Christie cruiser from Nuffield. Both featured complex experimental transmission and steering systems but, had they been completed, neither would have been any better armed than the A9, even down to the two auxiliary machine-gun turrets. In the event two tanks – one pilot model of each – were submitted for trials in running order but without armament, and then abandoned. A large number of armoured vehicles that dated from the inter-war years were also still in service, but although they should not be forgotten, they

7 *The Nuffield heavy cruiser A16E1 on a trial run. All three turrets can be seen but no weapons are mounted.*

8 *Wearing British 'trade plates' the Czech TNH/P light tank during tests at the Mechanisation Experimental Establishment.*

have no direct bearing on the situation in 1939 except as training machines or last-ditch defenders in the event of invasion.

Another trend which manifested itself at this time was summed up in *The Business of Tanks* by Brigadier G Macleod Ross.* He quoted General Sir Campbell Clarke, one-time Deputy Director of Design, who said 'If you don't keep a firm hand on weapon policy on tactical grounds, the General Staff goes a-whoring after foreign weapons every few months, but it is useless to talk technicalities to them'. If the implication is that all foreign weapons were no good this is rather a sweeping statement – after all, there was not much wrong with the Besa, Bren or Bofors guns – but it does contain a kernel of truth. So far as tanks are concerned it should be taken as meaning that when the General Staff found itself beseiged by technical problems which it did not understand it tended to

*G. Macleod Ross, *The Business of Tanks*, A. H. Stockwell Ltd. 1976

9 *The Hotchkiss H39 tank at Farnborough during MEE evaluation trials.*

assume that foreign designers had already solved them, and started shopping around. Two examples can be cited. In March 1939 a Praga model TNH/P tank, weighing 8 tons, was imported from Czechoslovakia by Morris-Commercial. Trials at MEE proved that in general it was a fine design and the tracks, in particular, were considered to be very good indeed. Its greatest fault was a tactical one: the gun mounting was designed in such a way that it had to be locked before the main armament, a 37mm gun, could be fired. Since the suspension was rather harsh this meant that the tank could only fire accurately when it was stationary, apart from with its machine gun. The Royal Tank Corps was trained to shoot on the move – the very essence of tank fighting in British eyes – and as the Czech tank failed on that score it was rejected. About a year later a French tank, the Hotchkiss model H39, was examined as a possible infantry tank and, it seems, some important business interests were involved. The evaluation team was impressed by the use of large castings to form the hull and turret. They liked its power and armour protection but again felt that the suspension was not forgiving enough on difficult ground. They failed to comment on its worst feature, the two-man crew. One was the driver, but the commander occupied a one-man turret where he had to direct the tank, load and fire the main armament and the machine gun as well. The A11 must have seemed child's play by comparison. In the event the reason given for rejecting the French deal was the worsening international situation; how much more would this have applied to the Czech design.

2 And then there were none

10   *Light tanks Mark VIB of 2nd Battalion, Royal Tank Regiment travel as deck cargo with their crews* en route *for France, and disaster.*

A generation after their fathers had done so the young men of a new British Expeditionary Force crossed the English Channel to France. At first the tanks were sent by a longer route and landed on the west coast around Brest and St Nazaire while their crews took the short sea route. By the end of September 1939 the first elements were moving into line on the frontier. Later, when it was clear that there was no immediate likelihood of enemy interference, both men and machines used the short cross-Channel route.

With the Germans fully occupied in Poland there was a breathing space of nine months which enabled the forces to build up to strength, train and try to work out a concerted plan with their French allies. By May 1940 these

units of the Royal Armoured Corps were on French soil (although in many cases still not up to full establishment): 1st Fife and Forfar Yeomanry, 1st East Riding Yeomanry, 5th Royal Inniskilling Dragoon Guards, 15th/19th The King's Royal Hussars, 4th/7th Royal Dragoon Guard, 13th/18th Royal Hussars, and the 1st Lothian and Border Yeomanry. These were divisional cavalry regiments, the first four of which soon formed 1st and 2nd Light Armoured Reconnaissance Brigades while the others were not brigaded. Each regiment was equipped with twenty-eight Light Mark VI tanks and forty-four Scout Carriers. In addition there was the 12th Royal Lancers, the only armoured-car regiment, equipped with thirty-eight of the Morris light armoured reconnaissance cars. These were backed up by the 1st Army Tank Brigade, comprising the 4th Royal Tank Regiment (RTR) with fifty A11 infantry tanks and five light tanks, and the 7th Royal Tank Regiment with twenty-seven A11s, twenty-three A12 Matildas and seven light tanks. The Brigade's third regiment, the 8th Royal Tanks, remained in Britain with hardly a tank to its name. Making ready to leave for France was the 1st Armoured Division, which is discussed later.

In addition, each infantry battalion was equipped with ten Bren Gun Carriers, and two platoons of the 4th Battalion, Royal Northumberland Fusiliers could boast some of the new Daimler scout cars. The 2nd Battalion, Queen Victoria's Rifles and 5th Battalion, The Loyal Regiment had also been issued with scout cars but were obliged to hand them over to the 1st Armoured Division. Finally, six Guy Mark I armoured cars formed the Phantom Squadron of No 3 Air Mission for special liaison duties with GHQ. It would not be out of place to emphasise that of a grand total of 308 tanks listed here only twenty-three were equipped with 2-pounder guns. All the rest had machine guns only, which proved perfectly useless as anti-tank weapons. Of course these twenty-three Matildas didn't stand alone against the Panzer Divisions – the French Army fielded well over 3000 modern gun-armed tanks. However, because of their deployment and poor tactical handling they turned out to be largely a wasted asset.

Most of the BEF went into line on the Belgian frontier between the French Seventh and First armies. The British soldiers found themselves in surroundings familiar to them from their father's tales. Names like Loos, Lens and La Bassee suddenly became a reality, while the scars of that earlier conflict were still plainly visible, as were the massive, well-tended graveyards. Yet the BEF didn't need these tangible reminders of the Great War. It remained firmly embedded in the subconscious of those charged with guiding Britain's fortunes; not all the lessons of the years between could erase it. The great mock battles on Salisbury Plain that had, so recently, seemed to herald a new era of mechanised armoured warfare suddenly appeared to be no more than so much naive play-acting. The shades of the Somme rose to haunt men's minds with dark images of the trenches and, for a while, developed into a strange sub-plot.

Dealing with this theme in terms of armoured warfare one can watch it at work. On the surface was the mainstream reality in the form of increased tank production. It was consistent and logical, if not particularly imaginative. Construction of existing designs went ahead while improved models were conceived, developed and evaluated with an increasing sense of urgency. Beneath the surface other forces were at work, stimulated by the idea that we were back where we had been in 1915, in more senses than one, with the slaughter about to begin again.

To the south of the British position lay the Maginot Line, the ultimate entrenchment. To the east was the Siegfried Line which was seen, at the time, as the German equivalent. If these two lines were to form the boundaries of a new Western Front then the ground between them must be the new no-man's-land, to be battered to pulp by heavy artillery; not at all the sort of ground that modern tanks had been designed to operate over. Furthermore, if this war was to develop along the same lines as the last one this entire region would become virtually impassable in winter as rain filled the shell holes of a pockmarked landscape while men and tanks floundered. So, having paid lip service, and very little else to the modern creed of mobile armoured warfare the General Staff began to wonder if it was the way forward after all. What if this war proved to be a continuation of the last one, the kind of war they had experienced? Better perhaps to play safe and take another look at tank design based on the premise that the First World War might start all over again.

By the end of September 1939 outline specifications had been drawn up for a tank to be known as A20 which was, in effect, a modernised version of the Mark VIII International of 1918. It was to be a good deal larger than anything currently in production, capable of leading a direct assault upon enemy positions and, most important of all, able to operate over very soft ground in winter. In terms of armour protection A20 had to withstand attack by the current German anti-tank gun, the 37mm; it should be able to travel at 10 mph and, as ever, be transportable by rail. Above all it should exert the lowest possible ground-pressure and be designed in such a way that it could employ an unditching beam. In stressing this last requirement the General Staff had to accept that the tank would be turretless so that the reversion to First World War principles was almost complete. Since side sponsons were the obvious answer it was planned that each one would mount a 2-pounder gun with a coaxial Besa while a third Besa and a two-inch smoke projector would be fitted in the front of the hull, alongside the driver.

A feasibility study was carried out by the Mechanisation Board and Vickers which soon resulted in revised specifications. For one thing the idea of using secondary tracks beneath the belly of the tank, as on the proposed Flying Elephant tank of 1916, was dropped. The Mechanisation Board pointed out that the required immunity could not be provided on such a large tank without seriously affecting the ground pressure, so a 60mm armour basis was agreed upon, proof against the 37mm shell but not the anti-tank shot. Also, they said, a turret was in every way preferable to sponsons, but even then a total weight of around 32 tons must be anticipated. Leslie Little, the chief designer at Vickers, simply said that the General Staff should outline their requirements as broadly as possible and leave his firm to carry out the design work and settle the details. Subsequently the Director of Mechanisation put forward a design for a tank, armoured to 60mm standard, with the turret and armament of the A12 Matilda and the engine and transmission of the new Covenanter cruiser. On this basis, it was suggested, there would be no need to build pilot models since the major components were already tried and tested. This was a dangerous precedent.

By the end of October outline drawings were nearing completion and the Belfast shipbuilders, Harland and Wolff, had been approached as potential manufacturers. Production of up to 100 machines was envisaged and the firm hoped that they would be able to persuade the authorities to adopt a new 300 hp diesel engine of their own design. By January 1940 it was decided that the first two tanks should be completed in mild steel – in effect pilot models after all – and that the Meadows flat 12-cylinder petrol engine developed for Covenanter would be used since the Harland engine was not yet available. It was still the period of the 'Phoney War', but production was not expected to be complete before 1941.

From this point matters began to deteriorate. At a series of weekly meetings the main order was cancelled and reinstated while the number of pilots was increased to four, then six and back to four again. The proposed armament became a contentious issue when the new 6-pounder gun and a French 75mm howitzer were considered. Since neither of them would fit into a Matilda turret it was planned to mount the chosen one alongside the driver. It was then discovered that the 6-pounder barrel would stick out in front of the tank where it was likely to be damaged. Attempts to shorten it were defeated on the grounds of reduced performance and the same problem was encountered when a naval anti-torpedo boat gun of the same calibre was suggested. The French weapon was rejected on the dubious grounds that the front of the tank would have to be redesigned to accept it. Ultimately it was agreed that the 3-inch howitzer would be used.

Early in 1940 an approach was made to Vauxhall Motors with a view to including them in the production programme. They were also invited to develop an alternative engine. The Ministry of Supply would build and equip a new factory for them at Luton. Despite the fact that they had no experience of tank building, or indeed of heavy engineering on this scale, the firm agreed, and set to work to produce a suitable power unit. They were hampered by the need to make it fit into the existing space in the vehicle, but in a remarkably short space of time had developed a flat–12 petrol engine based on Bedford components. The transmission question arose again. It was felt that the Wilson system originally specified might prove too complicated, and at this time the War Office was showing a great deal of interest in a novel gearbox known as the Sinclair Powerflow. Indeed at one stage it was hoped that the Sinclair would replace the Wilson transmission in all British tanks. At first sight it seemed ideal. The Sinclair system operated through a fluid clutch and featured what was described as a traction gear, which came into play during the gear-changing process. Instead of the pause that normally occurs when a vehicle is moving from one gear to the next, the action in a Sinclair box brought another clutch into play which maintained the drive and actually continued to accelerate the vehicle while a gear-change was taking place. The only drawback was that the inventor never quite got the thing to work properly, so it was never adopted, although it appeared again, briefly, in 1945. Eventually a combined gearbox and steering system known as the Merritt-Brown was chosen, the invention of Dr Merritt of the David Brown Company. Such a system is described as regenerative, since when a tank is turning no power is wasted by being directed to the slower-moving track. Instead, as the steering brake is applied a train of gears ensures that the surplus power only goes to the driven track, thus enhancing the turning movement.

The suspension chosen for the A20 appears to have derived from one tested on a pre-war A7 medium tank. It consisted of pairs of small-diameter rollers on trailing arms, acting on short coil-springs, with fourteen such bogies on each side. Apart from these rollers the entire suspension system was protected by external plating, although the top run of the track was exposed. Crew access hatches were provided in each side of the hull, near the front, while above and behind them were apertures for Besa machine-guns, the last vestige of the old sponson idea. By May 1940 there was talk of two more pilots with new-style turrets, presumably with a view to mounting a larger gun, but already events were unfolding in France that would render the entire project redundant. The first pilot model, A20E1, was ready for trials although gearbox trouble brought these to a premature end. Still they seemed to show that the basic design was quite workable and the tank was completed to the point of fitting a Matilda turret. In this form it weighed forty tons and carried a crew of seven. As usual it was gloomily pointed out that it was far too heavy to operate over existing military bridges. The second pilot model, which mounted a temporary wooden superstructure in place of the turret, went to Luton for examination by Vauxhall. There is no clear evidence to indicate whether the Bedford engine was fitted but it is known that the tracks were reversed, in keeping with current thinking. At this stage Britain's first attempt in this war to produce a heavy assault tank was terminated.

Some six weeks after the General Staff initiated the A20 project it was approached by another individual who had been thinking along the same lines. This was none other than Sir Albert Stern, one-time secretary of the First World War Landships Committee, whose considerable strength of character and forthright manner had virtually forced the British Army to adopt tanks in 1916. That he still retained these attributes in full measure was soon clear, although they hardly accorded with the requirements of a good committee man. As author of his own legend Stern was convinced that he, and he alone, could pull off the same trick, again. In order to strengthen his hand he had even gathered around him most of the men

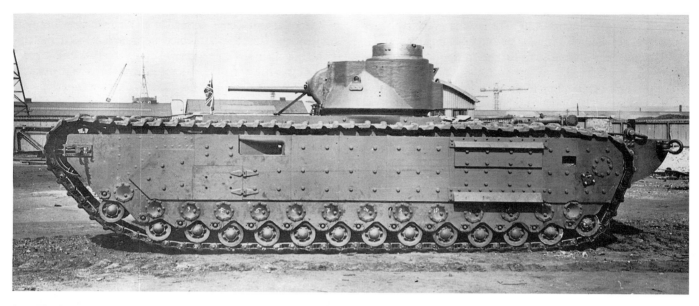

11 *The heavy tank A20, mounting a Matilda turret, and probably photographed at the Harland & Wolff shipyard in Belfast. The slot in the side, just above the hull access door, marks the location of a Besa machine-gun.*

– technical experts and military visionaries – who had worked with him on those first tanks: W G Wilson, Sir William Tritton, Harry Ricardo, Sir Ernest Swinton, Sir Eustace Tennyson D'Eyncourt and others. With this list in his pocket he persuaded the Cabinet to back him and formed the experts into the Special Vehicle Development Committee (SVDC) or, as it soon came to be known, The Old Gang.

One suspects that the General Staff was not terribly impressed, and it may well be that some members of the committee had been pressganged into joining. Most of them were beyond retiring age and doubtless found the experience rejuvenating, but Ricardo and Wilson were still busy men and it is curious to note that Wilson's speciality, the epicyclic transmission, played no part in the new scheme. Instead The Old Gang opted for petrol-electric drive, a system Stern had stubbornly tried to promote in 1916. He had lost that battle to Wilson and it is possible that he was not above trying to get his own back, even after all this time.

Work on their first tank began in February 1940 with the construction of a wooden mock-up and the ordering of parts. These included a Paxman 12-cylinder diesel engine and nickel-steel track plates to the same design as those used on the very first tanks. Clearly Stern's gang believed that trench warfare conditions would reassert themselves, that tank design had taken the wrong direction since 1919 and that they were the only people with the experience to put things right. Inevitably the contract for building this huge tank went to Tritton's firm, William Foster & Co of Lincoln, where the first tanks were made, and by May 1940 the order was increased to two, which became known as TOG 1 and TOG 2 respectively. Another Great War veteran, C H Merz of Merz and

McLellan, was responsible for the design of the electric drive equipment, although it was manufactured by the English Electric Company.

One look at the mock-up of TOG 1 was sufficient to prove beyond doubt where its origins lay. The tall, narrow hull retained the rhomboid shape of its ancestors and the effect was enhanced by the oldfashioned track plates and the machine-gun sponsons at the sides (although these were never fitted to the prototype). As a concession to progress a French 75mm howitzer was mounted in the front of the hull and a Matilda turret on top. Compared with A20, TOG was to be very well armoured, sufficient to withstand a hit from a 47mm armour-piercing round, although the exact arrangements were never finalised. The prototype was seen with massive panels of imitation armour, about 65mm thick, fitted to the sides. The first trial took place in the works yard and adjacent test field on 27 September 1940. An opportunity was taken to weigh the righthand side of the tank which tipped the scales at 36 tons 14 cwt, from which it was not difficult to work out that the whole machine weighed over 73 tons at this stage. And that was before any weapons or real armour had been fitted, or the tank was stowed and crewed for action.

On 6 October the first official demonstration took place before a specially invited party that included all members of the SVDC except, it should be noted, Wilson. His professional relationship with Stern had never been a very easy one, made all the more difficult by the fact that Stern had no technical training at all, certainly not in the highly specialised field of tank transmissions. Indeed, it is worth recording that in June Stern had inspected the new Merritt-Brown transmission for A20 at Woolwich and pronounced it as quite useless for operating in wet mud!

Like its official cousin A20, TOG 1 ceased to have any validity when Hitler's Panzers were loosed on France. Yet no attempt appears to have been made to bring the project to a halt. Trials continued until June 1941 and even then it was modified to accept a hydraulic drive system. During this period most of the teething troubles were eliminated although the tank was always difficult to steer, due to the long stretch of track in contact with the ground. This was further aggravated by the fact that, like its First World War predecessors, TOG 1 had no sprung suspension at all. It is also clear that the electric driving motors were prone to over-heating. As late as 28 May 1941 a trial was interrupted at various intervals in order to let the motors cool down.

Conversion to hydraulic drive took nearly two years: it was May 1943 before the tank – now redesignated TOG 1A – made its first run. The new equipment was manufactured by the Hydraulic Coupling and Engineering Company, and once again it echoed a scheme that had been tried and found wanting in 1917. After a month of intensive testing at Lincoln the tank went back into the factory for further modifications which resulted in orders being placed for some new parts in July. It appears to have remained there for some time since the next entry in its log records more minor alterations carried out in the spring of 1944. Once it was ready TOG 1A was moved to Chobham on the enormous Pickfords 100-ton transporter. It was never heard of again.

TOG 2 was ordered on 6 May 1940. It is not clear now why a new design was deemed necessary at such an early stage but the most likely reason concerned the armament. Certainly in terms of mechanical layout it was similar to TOG 1, and the most obvious difference was in the layout of the tracks. The actual plates were still of the First World War pattern and no form of suspension was employed, but the hull was arranged in such a way that the top run of the tracks, after they had passed around the front idlers, were led downwards through tunnels before rising again to pass around the drive sprockets at the rear. The object of this can only have been to permit a much larger turret-ring to be fitted on top of the hull, unrestricted by the tracks. The original wooden mock-up of the fighting compartment shows a 3-inch howitzer fitted in the front of the hull to the right of the driver, with sponsons on each side mounting a pair of Besa machine-guns. The turret is a box-like affair which looks like a larger version of the type later fitted to the Churchill Mark III. This contains an unusual triple gun-mounting, mentioned again in Chapter 4, consisting of another 3-inch howitzer, with a 2-pounder anti-tank gun to its right and a Besa on the left. By 1940 standards this would have been a formidable armament for any tank, but the machine itself was so big that it did not look out of place. Naturally armour protection was also on a grand scale for that time: surviving records speak of 2½-inch (63mm) cast-iron mock armour plates being prepared for the sides.

12   TOG 1 manoeuvring in Fosters' yard at Lincoln. This view shows the hull-mounted howitzer and the Matilda turret, not yet fitted with weapons. The other strange fitting is an inclinometer, for the benefit of the audience, mounted on the side.

13 *The full-size wooden mock-up of TOG2—at least the front half of it—fairly bristles with firepower. There is a 3-inch howitzer in the hull, another in the turret along with a 2-pounder and machine-gun, and a pair of machine-guns in sponsons at each side. The design would be modified several times before it was abandoned.*

When the tank ran for the first time, on 16 March 1941, neither the hull gun, side sponsons nor mock armour were fitted – only a wooden turret. Even so it weighed over 48 tons. These trials revealed the usual batch of minor problems but no mention is made of the overheating which still plagued TOG 1. By the end of the month the dummy turret had been replaced by a cast-iron ballast block which brought the overall weight up to 62 tons. In May 1941, with a wooden turret fitted again, the tank was moved to Farnborough for trials and, on its return to Lincoln in June, a new type of track was ordered. This was of a cast, open-web pattern in manganese steel. The tank was then photographed with what appears to be an even bigger fabricated-steel turret mounting a three-inch, 20 cwt anti-aircraft gun. At this time it was also painted in a three-colour disruptive camouflage scheme. Among the surviving drawings of TOG 2 there is one which shows how it would look when fitted with the turret of the contemporary American M6 heavy tank, which mounted a similar weapon.

In September 1941 further modifications were specified, of sufficient magnitude to warrant a change of title. From now on the tank would be known as TOG 2★. By this time the idea of mounting a gun in the front of the hull and fitting side sponsons had definitely been dropped and the armour arrangements were changed accordingly. There were further substantial modifications to the final drive but the most important change was a decision to adopt a sprung, torsion-bar suspension, although this was not fitted until April 1943. In the meantime yet another style of turret had been fitted. Designed to mount the new 17-pounder anti-tank gun and developed by Messrs Stothert and Pitt of Bath, it served as the pattern for the

turret which would eventually be mounted on the A30 Challenger tank in 1944. Another curious change had taken place in October 1942 when the tracks were removed and replaced back to front, just as they had been on the A20, so that now the raised lip on each link was to the rear when the track lay on the ground.

Trials continued without any undue problems throughout May 1943. The tank was regarded as virtually complete although it now weighed approximately 80 tons. At a trial before most of the members of The Old Gang on 27 May 1943 it performed without a hitch, but there was no sign of the War Office wishing to place any orders. In due course it went down to Chobham for official trials but by now it was far too late. Plans had been prepared for a shorter version called TOG 2R (Revised) and a TOG 3 was even mooted, although neither were developed. Like the A20 the TOG tanks were built for a war that would never happen, or rather for a war than had happened over twenty years before. Yet it is interesting to note that these tanks lasted long enough to overlap the development of the German Tiger tanks – which were built in response to a different problem – and the even bigger Maus which, in a sense, they resembled. Like this latter machine much of the weight of the TOG tanks was due to the bulky propulsion system, allied to the need to keep ground pressure to a minimum, but in terms of armour protection they were no great improvement on Matilda. It is claimed in their favour that they provided a great deal of valuable information on design technology to British engineers, although there is no evidence to show that they made very much use of it. In retrospect the TOG tanks appear only as a frightful waste of precious resources at a time when the country could least afford it.

The relationship between the Special Vehicle Department Committee and the Tank Board was always a difficult one. At a fairly early stage Sir Albert Stern had brought along a film to one of their meetings which demonstrated the performance of the Medium C, or Hornet tank of 1918, in the pious hope that this would help to establish his credentials. However, the discussions that took place after he had explained his ideas and withdrawn would probably have made his ears burn. During Sir James Lithgow's short term as chairman Stern actually had a seat on the board, but there is no reason to suppose that the other members took much heed of what he had to say. The SVDC was very much an ideas forum. Once it had drawn up outline specifications others took over the main task of translating them into engineering reality. As a consequence there were sometimes periods when The Old Gang had very little to do. Yet Stern continued to press his case and, when the Tank Board met to discuss proposals for a new type of cruiser tank (although it hardly matched up to his ideas of what a tank should be), he offered the services of his committee as the design team; an offer that was firmly turned down.

On 10 May 1940, during that fateful month when the

Germans demonstrated how armour should be correctly employed, Winston Churchill became Prime Minister. Until that time he had served as First Lord of the Admiralty, the office he held in 1915 which had caused him to become involved in the genesis of the tank. Writing after the Second World War he frankly confessed that by 1940 he was out of touch with AFV development, but it is an odd claim. As Chancellor of the Exchequer in the late 1920s he had presided over, and taken a great deal of interest in, military matters including the Experimental Armoured Force which, to some extent, had taught the Germans what they were now practising. But he, too, had been deeply affected by the squalid slaughter of the First World War and at this point, it seems, his faith in the potency of tanks was at a very low ebb. His pundits told him that in modern warfare, as represented by the Maginot Line, they would be useless. The depth of the defences would prove too tough to crack and modern artillery would obliterate them in the fire-swept zones between the lines. While still at the Admiralty Churchill cast about for an answer. It seemed to him that since the Maginot Line was primarily an underground system it followed that fighting on the surface was asking for trouble. Clearly the age of subterranean warfare had arrived. What was needed was a machine that could protect itself, and the rest of the army, by burrowing beneath the ground: a sort of land submarine. He gave his idea the codename White Rabbit, thinking, no doubt, of the creature in *Alice in Wonderland*, and in November 1939 he presented the problem to Sir Stanley Goodall, the Director of Naval Construction (DNC). For a while it must have seemed like 1915 all over again with Sir Stanley – as successor to Sir Eustace Tennyson D'Eyncourt – and his department ready to settle the technical details. All they had to do was design a machine that could dig a trench for itself and burrow its way across no-man's-land, preferably overnight. Along the trench in perfect safety would follow parties of infantry and if necessary tanks, to storm the enemy positions without once showing their heads above ground. Benefitting from the lessons of 1916 Churchill saw that surprise would be the key factor, and this time he proposed that a large number should be used, all at the same time, to smash the enemy line once and for all. The DNC formed a team under one of his department heads, C J W Hopkins, and enlisted the help of the Lincolnshire company Ruston-Bucyrus who manufactured most of the heavy earthmoving equipment produced in Britain.

A series of six designs under the codename Cultivator was drawn up and a scale model of the last of these was made by Bassett-Lowke, the famous model railway company. This was demonstrated to senior British and French officers and statesmen in an Admiralty cellar but, in April 1940, the entire project was handed over to the War Office. No doubt the Admiralty realised that if history repeated itself too faithfully it would find itself sad-

dled, once again, with a major land warfare project which was none if its business. The sensible thing to do was to get out of it sooner rather than later, even if it meant sacrificing the services of a valuable design team.

First hand experience of Blitzkrieg in May should have put an end to the scheme there and then, but with Churchill now in Downing Street and apparently as keen as ever it was not allowed to die. Instead it grew: two types were now envisaged, a narrow 'Private' machine for the infantry and a wider 'Officer' model to prepare trenches for tanks. But there were complications. The original plan had been to build relatively small machines, each powered by a single Rolls-Royce Merlin engine, which would not only move the thing along on its tracks but power the digging machinery as well. Now, with the Luftwaffe ready to strike from just across the Channel, the Royal Air Force needed every aircraft it could get and was not disposed to release precious engines to the army. A revised design centred round the massive Paxman-Ricardo diesel engine, but this increased the weight to such an extent that one engine could not perform both tasks. The only alternative was to use two engines, one to dig and one to drive, but this pushed the weight up even more.

The fall of France and the possibility that sensitive papers may have fallen into German hands led to the abandonment of Cultivator as the codename, and word was put about that the project had been abandoned altogether. In reality, it continued in secret under a new name, Nellie, derived from the initials of Naval Land Equipment, its formal name. Hopkins's team had already calculated that the most one could expect was a sub-surface speed of less than one mile per hour, but since the original reason for its development had vanished this hardly seemed to matter. The question was, what else could Nellie be used for? If the next stage in the German plan was an invasion of Britain it might prove useful for digging anti-tank ditches across southern England. It could also be used to tear up vulnerable airfields that might otherwise fall into enemy hands, or even to clear paths through minefields. The difficulty here was that the machine had been designed specifically to dig in the light, loamy soil of northern France; much of southern England is solid chalk, another matter altogether.

The first pilot model, a narrow infantry machine, was ready for trials by April 1941 – no mean engineering achievement considering the revolutionary nature of the design, but by then almost every reason for building it had gone, and the original order was cut back drastically. The finished machine weighed 131 tons, was 77 ft 6 ins long, 10 ft 6 ins high and just over 7 ft wide in the body. It came in two jointed sections. Nellie 1 was the nose, which housed the rotary earth cutters and conveyors to dispose of loose soil. It was located behind an 18 ft 6 ins wide plough blade at the front. Nellie 2 was the massive rear section which could be broken in half for transportation. It was a fully tracked vehicle, not unlike a giant

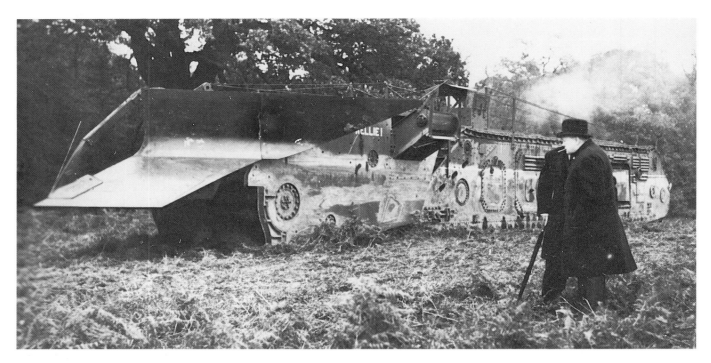

14 Winston Churchill watches as Nellie prepares for her trial run in Clumber Park, 6 November 1941. The commander's conning tower is visible on top of the hull, just behind the soil elevator.

First World War tank, containing the two 600hp engines, one behind the other. The leading engine drove the rotary cutter and conveyors in the nose by means of a flexible drive connection. The rear engine drove the tracks. There was an armoured conning tower for the commander with a driver's compartment below, but the body of the machine was not armoured, since while in the danger zone it should be protected by the very trench it was digging. On the surface it was steered by declutching one track, but in the trench this was achieved by hydraulically operated deflector plates pushing against the side of the cut, which literally forced the body out of alignment. The turning circle was calculated at one mile radius.

The pilot model concluded its trials quite successfully although the problems involved in just moving it around the country were daunting. Nellie had to be split into its three parts, the heaviest of which weighed 36 tons, and each part was carried on a large tracked trailer, hauled at an agonisingly slow speed by crawler tractors. Smaller parts, including hundreds of large bolts and some 120 track plates travelled in a fleet of lorries. An entire company of Royal Engineers was required to put it back together again, a process which took twenty-four hours.

As the war progressed the Nellie project became more and more divorced from reality, until by 1943 it was finally cancelled. By this time at least five machines had been built. Four were cut up in 1945 but another remained in store for some years before it, too, disappeared. It would

be consoling to be able to record that some benefit to the war effort resulted from this abortive scheme, but it is very difficult to find any. When digging a trench Nellie could shift earth at the rate of 8000 tons per hour – equivalent to the efforts of fourteen of the largest excavators then working in the country – but to no useful purpose. It was a brilliant engineering feat at a time when it might have been prudent to settle for more modest progress at a practical level.

From this first essay into what might have been we must now return to France on the eve of the German invasion. On 10 May the Germans started to move west. Declining to confront the Maginot fortifications their main armoured thrust wove its way through the supposedly tank-proof Ardennes Forest and outflanked them. In four days the German spearhead was effectively behind the British, to the north, and driving the French to the south and west. Meanwhile the BEF moved eastwards into Belgium until the leading light-tanks came up against a conventional German force. From this point the histories of all the British cavalry regiments seem to tell the same story, a repetitive saga of withdrawal from river line to river line, holding on for a while, blowing bridges then falling back. It is a tale of endless duels with German anti-tank guns that sliced clean through thin armour, of suicidal charges to destroy these guns by running over them, and even of scout carriers dashing into action like tanks. Regiments soon became squadrons or temporarily

15 Glenlyon, *an Infantry Tank Mark I of C squadron, 7th RTR, lies abandoned on a roadside near Arras. The turret is trained aft, all hatches are open and kit is strewn everywhere; evidence of a hasty departure. Another tank can be seen in the distance, just below the aerial.*

16 *Matildas* Glanton *and* Gloucester *having been abandoned in soft ground and set on fire by their crews are photographed by the Germans. The heavy castings protecting the co-axial Vickers guns identify these tanks as Mark Is.*

amalgamated until the few surviving machines were destroyed by their crews at Dunkirk.

Further south, a total of seven Panzer divisions burst out of the Ardennes to confront the Allies. Among these were the infantry tanks of the 1st Army Tank Brigade, concentrated for a counterstroke. The speed of the German advance sowed confusion everywhere and the British tanks found themselves directed first one way and then the other. Soon all movement had to be made by road as the railway system collapsed, and the tanks simply wore themselves out. It was the precious Matilda IIs that

suffered most – their smooth tracks wore down rapidly on paved roads or churned helplessly in the mud while the steering gear began to fail from overuse. It was only on 20 May when the then Brigadier Pope arrived to take a grip on things that this futile milling about ended. By this time the two battalions – as the 4th and 7th RTRs still chose to call themselves – had been reduced to fifty eight A11s and eighteen A12 Matildas. The 8th RTR, the third element in 1st Army Tank Brigade, never even got to France: production of A12s was so slow – due to the time required to make each one – that it could not be equipped in time.

The counterstroke, when it came, gave Rommel's 7th Panzer Division a fright, but it was almost a blow into thin air. The infantry tanks with their few lighter companions were given a series of objectives southwards from Vimy in the direction of Arras, but the distances were unrealistic. Even so they cut decisively through the unarmoured tail of 7th Panzer division, bringing the forward elements to a halt and causing a shockwave that went clear back to Berlin. They had neither the ammunition nor the reserves for a decisive breakthrough, and ended up under the muzzles of artillery and 88mm anti-aircraft guns directed by Rommel himself. There followed a fighting retreat into the Dunkirk perimeter and, ultimately, the loss of every single tank.

Two armoured brigades composed 1st Armoured Division. The 2nd Armoured Brigade consisted of the Bays, 10th Hussars and 9th Lancers; 3rd Armoured Brigade included 2nd, 3rd and 5th Royal Tank Regiments. The composition of the Bays was four A9 cruisers, three A10s and twenty-two A13s, with twenty-one Light Mark VIC tanks. This may be taken as typical. However, many of the cruiser tanks were so recently issued that their crews had only been half trained on them, and many lacked wireless sets, sighting telescopes and even armour-piercing ammunition. Besides the obvious disadvantage of working without a wireless the unfortunate tank had to carry ballast of equal weight, just to balance the turret. The division also went to France without most of its supporting elements of infantry and artillery. It was a time for panic measures. Most of the division's regiments began to arrive in France through Cherbourg in late May. By that time the German advance, westwards to the Somme and then north to the Channel coast, had effectively sealed it off from any chance it might have had to join up with the rest of the BEF except 3rd RTR which was simply thrown away. Detached from 3rd Armoured Brigade, this regiment went via Dover to Calais, where it landed on 22 May. Disorderly loading and the loss of much ancillary equipment led to chaos in the French port and delayed compliance with an order to drive straight for St Omer. When eventually it was ready, the regiment advanced about six miles and then ran into strong enemy forces, which accounted for about one third of the cruiser tank strength. Falling back on Calais amid streams of refugees the remaining tanks became involved in some costly street-fighting, for which they were not trained, and sacrificed more tanks following a premature order to destroy them. Calais fell on 26 May, by which time every one of 3rd RTR's tanks had been lost.

The remaining five regiments of 1st Armoured Division were concentrated west of the Seine, near Paris, by 23 May but they were soon ordered forward to the Somme. At this time the Germans were hovering around Dunkirk and holding the Somme line, pending a renewal of the offensive. Both British brigades struck hard, but lost many irreplaceable tanks in the process without causing the Germans much distress. When the enemy advance resumed on 5 June it turned into a grim race between 7th Panzer Division and the depleted British regiments to see who could get to Cherbourg first. It was another series of battles on the river lines; the British and French lost the battles but won the race.

It remains to record one more unhappy event in this sorry chapter. The Infantry Motor Battalions that had been separated from 1st Armoured Division when it went to France were needed for another purpose, the landings in Norway in response to the bold and successful German invasion. The area chosen was the sparsely populated mountainous region around Narvik in the north and the slightly more inviting landscape at Trondheim further south. Narvik was to be the main focus of attention but it was not considered to be 'tank country' and, in any case, there were hardly any to spare. A few light tanks belonging to 3rd Hussars were sent aboard the Polish transport *Chobry*, but they never landed. The ship was bombed and sunk, but most of the men were saved, including a large number from 1st Battalion the Irish Guards. With the ship sinking and on fire, and with most senior officers already dead the Guards formed up on deck with full kit and then steadily boarded a destroyer which came alongside. As an example of pure discipline it has been compared to the sinking of the *Birkenhead* in 1852.

British armour had faced its first serious test in action for over twenty years and it had failed. It was not necessarily because the Germans had better or more reliable machines, or even that they outnumbered the British – the French fielded more tanks than Britain and Germany put together. It was certainly not because, man for man, the Panzer troops were better than those of the Royal Armoured Corps, although it would be fair to say that with the Polish campaign behind them German troops had had more immediate battle experience, while many British soldiers had only just been introduced to their tanks. The real problem was to do with tactical handling and cooperation with the other services. The pre-war British tendency was to treat each arm of service as an independent part, while the Germans preached harmony. Blitzkrieg demanded close cooperation between tanks and infantry supported by the artillery and the Luftwaffe's Stuka divebombers.

17 A Scammell 20-ton tank-transporter weaves its way through refugee traffic in Le Neuborg carrying a Cruiser Mark IV of 1st Armoured Division. A few more of these vehicles could have saved the BEF a lot of tanks, at least in the short term.

18 A spot of maintenance work in a French farmyard for a Morris armoured car of 12th Lancers.

19 The 15mm Besa gun identifies this armoured car as a Guy Mark 1A. It is seen near Bovington on a training run.

20 *Scout Carriers in France with their Boys rifles at the ready. The second vehicle also mounts a Bren light machine-gun.*

Inevitably there had to be an inquest and, since most of those involved had not yet grasped the real implications of what had happened, it was equally inevitable that the initial blame should fall upon the tools. So how had they acquitted themselves?

The 12th Lancers had few kind words to say about their Morris armoured cars. Built on to an ordinary truck chassis they did not perform well off the road, and the bulky body made them difficult to turn round in a hurry. The open turret gave no overhead protection and the firepower of one Boys anti-tank rifle and a Bren gun was only acceptable in the reconnaissance role for which they were designed. Fighting rearguard actions, as they were obliged to in France, they were totally inadequate. The little Daimler scout car came off much better. For one thing its very size made it unsuitable for anything but reconnaissance, while one hand-held Bren gun was neither potent nor accurate enough for anything else. Among the requirements called for afterwards was a secure mounting for the gun to improve accuracy, and the abandonment of four-wheel steering. After extensive use, especially across country, it became so stiff as to be unusable, and conventional steering was preferred. For all that it was highly manoeuvrable, easy to conceal and yet able to tackle the most rugged country. The preselector gearbox made it far less tiring to drive and although there were some cooling problems it was generally very reliable. Phantom Squadron, in its history,* makes no mention of the Guy armoured car but enough adverse reports were coming in from a trials unit in the Middle East. These concerned the axles, differential gears and wheelbearings, all of

*R J T Hills, *Phantom was There*, Edward Arnold, 1951.

which failed in service. This was allied to a severe twisting of the chassis frame which had the unfortunate effect of bending the selector rods and making it impossible to change gear.

Tracked vehicles also came in for a fair dose of criticism. The Scout and Bren carriers had performed well enough, being reliable if vulnerable and subject to overloading. Like the wheeled reconnaissance vehicles they had been seriously misused in the field, particularly when they were sent to take on anti-tank guns singlehanded. The same could be said of the light tanks. For recce work during an advance they might be admirable, although they were regarded as uneconomical compared with armoured cars, but as a rear-guard they were of very dubious value. Even so, had they been used wisely, staying mobile and prodding for weak spots upon which to launch a counter-attack they might have done some good. As it was they came under the orders of senior commanders who had little idea of how to employ tanks at all, let alone to differentiate between the various types and use each correctly. For this the blame must lie with a shortsighted high command which could see no value in the appointment of a senior tank advisor at GHQ who might make a stand against foolish deployment. Generally the light tanks seem to have been reliable – tracks and suspension stood up to the wear very well, while the Meadows engine behaved well and delivered plenty of power. Their armour protection was insufficient to resist anything but small-arms fire, while their own most powerful weapon, the .5 inch Vickers machine gun, was notoriously unreliable.

Of the infantry tanks the little Mark I, or A11, was taking part in its first and last campaign. The premature death of Carden, its designer, has robbed us of the chance

21 *An abandoned Light Tank Mark VIC of HQ Squadron, 10th Hussars, with its turret reversed to show the two Besa machine-guns.*

to find out exactly what he had in mind when he designed it, but a fair guess might be that he visualised it as a well-protected mobile strongpoint; a means of giving the infantry an almost indestructable self-propelled machine-gun that would go anywhere they could. Yet in order to do this effectively it would have been necessary to produce many hundreds and employ them in vast swarms to overwhelm the opposition. Using them like that would not have made unreasonable demands on individual tank commanders, and backed up by some of their heavier brethren armed with 2-pounder guns they might have provided an answer to positional warfare. In mobile conditions, especially on the defensive against tanks, they were impotent and only inherent reliability and thick armour told in their favour.

In many ways the A12 Matilda was the outstanding tank of the campaign but the twenty-three of them were hopelessly outnumbered. And to make matters worse those twenty-three were fresh off the production line and quite new to their crews; both were untried in service. In combat they were all but invincible and the 2-pounder

gun mastered nearly everything it fired at. Only misused artillery or anti-aircraft guns stood any chance of knocking them out, and a good high-explosive round was the best answer to these. The 2-pounder could not deliver this, and the lack of a suitable dual-purpose weapon became something of a fixation with British tank men for the next two years. On the debit side, the Associated Equipment Company (AEC) diesels in these early models often proved troublesome. Complaints were also made about the gear-changing linkage, the Wilson gearbox which sometimes failed in second gear and the Rackham steering clutches which shed bolts. Most of this was due to excessive road-running when the railway system collapsed under enemy pressure. 1st Army Tank Brigade had no tank transporters at this stage, only a few Scammell recovery tractors which were used to tow some of the more mobile casualties. Difficulties with the early pattern-tracks have already been mentioned. In wet weather they lost traction and the immediate solution, welding steel bars to each link, was hardly ideal. Two other modifications carried out on 7th RTR's Matildas proved equally troublesome. The curious scuttle-shaped tail skids applied to some tanks were never needed, if only because the Germans were too busy advancing to dig the trenches which these attachments were designed to help the tanks across. Another expedient, that of jacking up the suspension by about six inches, presumably in order to give better ground clearance in soft going, placed an undue strain on the bogie actuating levers and caused them to fracture.

Among the cruiser tanks the Mark I, or A9, seems to have escaped comment altogether, probably because there were so few of them. Exact figures are not available but it seems reasonable to suppose that most of those sent out to France with 1st Armoured Division were of the close-support type which only appeared in small numbers with headquarters troops. Certainly the miserable armour protection would come in for some criticism and it would be surprising indeed if the occupants of the two auxiliary machine-gun turrets had anything complimentary to say about them. Presumably the complaints known to have been levelled at the Cruiser Mark II, or A10, applied equally to the A9, which shared many of its features. The A10 was better protected but only marginally heavier than the A9, so the comment that it was too slow – that the 150hp AEC engine was not powerful enough – must have been relevant in both cases, as were accusations of unreliability and even complete failure. It was also pointed out that the tracks came off too easily and, being of the double pin type, proved very difficult to replace in a hurry. They were also said to be too narrow for the weight, which increased ground pressure to an unacceptable level, and to give very poor grip across country due to their almost smooth surface.

The two versions of A13, Cruisers Mark III and IV, were the subjects of a list of failures. The Liberty engine appears to have enjoyed an average life of 100 hours while starter solenoids stuck repeatedly, or burnt out altogether. The main clutch often slipped due to overheating while the steering clutches failed consistently. But once again it was the tracks that were condemned most of all. They slipped in the wet, came off with tiresome regularity and shed connecting pins for a pastime. If they broke at speed they wrapped themselves around the road wheels or ripped off all the light metalwork along the side of the hull. An altogether more macabre fault lay in the design of the commander's cupola, a 12 inch high drum on top of the turret. When the tank was closed down in action the commander could still observe through visors in the cupola, but the entire assembly was, on occasion, swept clean off the turret by a direct hit, taking the commander's head with it. The effect on the morale of the rest of the crew need hardly be described. The tank's main asset, its high top speed, was of only limited use in close country, especially when fighting a defensive action, and its only value lay in its ability to keep ahead of the pursuing Germans. It was never admitted at the time but it is fair to say now that a proportion of these faults could be

22   An A13 Mark I (Cruiser Mark III) of 1st Armoured Division in France. Twin smoke dischargers are visible on the side of the turret.

blamed not only on the tanks. Crews with more experience of their charges soon got used to their more wayward traits and learned to detect and remedy them at an earlier stage. Except for the A11, the tanks used in France were also represented in the Western Desert, where they often travelled hundreds of miles on their own tracks without any trouble at all. This was partly due to less trying conditions but it had a lot more to do with a higher standard of maintenance and crew care.

On a more general level there was a natural reaction to thin armour which resulted in a demand for a minimum 40mm standard. Sighting telescopes steamed up too easily and the design of the power traverse equipment made it difficult to maintain. Even towropes did not escape comment. Those supplied with the cruiser tanks were not strong enough and broke regularly. Dread of the Stuka also led to a call for an anti-aircraft machine gun for the commander, a request that resulted in some weird and wonderful improvisations. In the long term these proved to be a wasted effort. Unlike their American counterparts British tank men soon came to the conclusion that it was better to batten down and wait until the thing went away, rather than try to shoot it down. Another point that arose from their experience in France was the matter of identification. British tanks all carried a painted white square on appropriate surfaces of the hull and turret so that it was readily visible from any angle, but there appears to have been no attempt made to harmonise with the Allies. The art of tank recognition was obviously in its infancy since incidents were reported during which British and French troops fired on British tanks which, in turn, shot up French tanks on occasion. Worse still, there were at least two occasions when RTR officers tried to halt or rally

23 A few light tanks like this Mark VIA were modified in the suspension to give a longer track base and hence a better ride. At least two served with 1st Armoured Division in France but this one was photographed in Britain. Extra shock absorbers have been fitted above the springs to reduce the incidence of pitching and note that this tank has no cupola on the turret.

German tanks, thinking they were British: they attributed their survival to quick reactions and the fact that RTR and Panzer troops both wore black overalls. Following these early actions a red and white recognition flash was suggested, and later adopted in the desert.

It would be wrong to pretend that German tanks were that much better. The two smallest models, Panzers I and II, were as poorly armed and armoured as similar British machines. The Panzer III was undergunned when compared with Matilda or the British cruisers and it suffered from recurring failures of the torsion bar suspension. The Panzer IV, equipped with a short 75mm gun, was intended for the close support of infantry and was generally used in that role, despite the fact that it could also fire an anti-tank round if required. The two impressed Czechoslovakian models, the 35(t) and 38(t) were tough on their crews, being cramped and very harsh on the suspension. The real advantage for the Germans was that if a German tank failed it could easily be recovered and repaired when the battle moved on, but if a British tank broke down, unless the crew could put it right at once, it was bound to fall into enemy hands. This is why the

British failed to capture a single German tank in France while the Germans gathered up a whole host of British machines. Indeed, they soon had parks full of light tanks, many of which could easily be restored to working order. Much worse, they had a few Matildas, which led them, if they had not realised it before, to appreciate the need for a much more powerful gun. That most insidious race which still plagues the tank world was on: up-gun and up-armour to stay ahead.

Without a captured German tank of their own to evaluate under controlled conditions the British could only fall back on rumours, highly coloured opinions and vivid imagination to explain their defeat. From this early debacle and news of similar events filtering back from Poland can be traced the origins of the Panzer myth that soon permeated all Allied armies to the end of the war and beyond. A formidable legend had been born.

On the other hand the lesson was lost on some, as this extract from a Royal Armoured Corps report of 1940 shows: 'Secondly, it is important not to allow ourselves to be carried away by the experiences gained in the very mobile operations of the Flanders fighting. Such fighting will doubtless recur, and we must be prepared for it: but if the war extends into 1941, a phase of positional warfare is inevitable and our long-range plan must prepare for that too. At present we have no tanks capable of operating in positional warfare'. It probably would have been more accurate to say that we hardly had any tanks at all.

3 The cupboard was bare

24 *Many of the armoured regiments raised or reforming in Britain after Dunkirk had to make do with whatever was available, and that was precious little. This one, for instance, musters an amazing collection; a 1920 Rolls-Royce armoured car, a six-wheeled Lanchester Mark IA of 1928, a Chrysler Airflow sedan with a Bren gun mounted in the sunshine roof and a Morris 15-cwt platoon truck similarly armed. A Standard Beaverette is driving by and it should be noted that all vehicles, except the Rolls-Royce, are fitted with radio.*

When the survivors of the British Expeditionary Force struggled home in June 1940 they brought back with them thirteen tanks – six light and seven cruisers. They left behind in France another 691, not counting armoured cars and carriers. All those rescued came from 1st Armoured Division. They joined 340 tanks and armoured cars – not including scout cars, carriers and obsolete training machines – still in the United Kingdom. Production of new tanks at this time was desperately slow; in the case of cruisers for example it was estimated at around sixteen per month. Things were looking grim.

Logically the next step for the Germans was a cross-Channel invasion and, if this was to be met with any degree of confidence, it was clear that a massive increase in armoured vehicle production had to begin at once. Various new models were in the pipeline: the Infantry Tank Mark III (Valentine) and Mark IV (Churchill); Cruisers Mark V and VI (Covenanter and Crusader), and a new light tank, the Mark VII (Tetrarch). All but the first named existed only as drawing-board projects or untried prototypes which could certainly not be counted on for

the time being. Developments were also taking place with armoured cars and a new type of carrier. Time was the most vital essential but no one could deny that time was one commodity that might not be available.

Among the survivors was the newly promoted Major-General Pope, breathing fire and urgency, demanding a new generation of tanks with thicker armour and more powerful guns. He placed the recently formed Tank Board in an immediate quandary. The problem was simple enough – either one swept the board clear, halted production and set about designing and building a whole range of new tanks to these specifications, or one let the existing programme stand with a view to building as many tanks, albeit inferior, as possible. It was considered that to produce a completely new kind of tank a gestation period of at least eighteen months was needed before production began. In the face of an enemy who had reduced a country the size of France in six weeks, it would be a brave man indeed who would sanction such a course. From the highest authority, Downing Street, came the decision to proceed with the current programme: to build tanks, any tanks, for the most urgent defence of the realm. From this directive stemmed a policy that inhibited British tank production until the end of the war. In the circumstances, however, it is difficult to see what else could have been done.

An immediate re-equipment programme was defined with the following priorities: to rebuild 1st Armoured Division and 1st Army Tank Brigade to full establishment with cruiser and infantry tanks respectively; to complete 2nd Armoured Division temporarily with light tanks; to raise three more army tank brigades, 21st, 23rd and 24th, and equip them with infantry tanks as these became available; and to provide all other armoured regiments already raised with anything that could be armoured and made to carry a gun.

The fulfilment of the first three objectives was only a matter of time, but that might not be available. The last could be achieved much more readily as long as one was not too fussy about what vehicles they were equipped with. Depots throughout the country were scoured for suitable, or even unsuitable, machines. Venerable armoured cars of the 1920s were dug out; Rolls-Royces, Lanchesters, Crossleys and even a few solid-tyred Peerlesses of 1919 vintage were coaxed into working order and handed over to units. Since their export trade had been summarily stopped by the war, Vickers-Armstrong was obliged to hand over any commercial tanks waiting for delivery, and small batches of two models were acquired. At major training centres like Bovington Camp the instructors were briefed on an emergency programme. In the event of invasion driver-training tanks would be hastily equipped with weapons and wireless sets from the various schools and made ready for action.

At the same time a number of motor manufacturers were asked to produce armoured versions of their basic commercial models. The Standard Motor Company responded with a lightly protected version of their regular 14hp saloon car. The result was a small, open topped vehicle for a crew of two, known as the Beaverette. The Rootes Group carried out a slightly more ambitious

conversion of their Humber Super Snipe resulting in the Humberette, otherwise known as the Ironside. Bedford used their 30cwt OX lorry chassis as the basis for the OXA which had a fully protected cab and a large, open fighting compartment at the back. The weapons available for this improvised fleet included Bren guns, Boys rifles

26 Canadian soldiers rigging a camouflage net over their Standard Beaverette Mark 2 which, despite its modest armour can hardly disguise its civilian origins.

25 A number of tanks on order from Vickers-Armstrong for foreign customers were impounded by the War Office for training. The one on the left in this picture is a light tank intended for the Dutch East Indies—and known to British troops as the Dutchman. It is followed by a Light Tank Mark II of 1931 vintage.

27 A Humber Light Reconnaissance Car Mark I on test. These cars had a top speed of 45 mph despite the extra armour.

and Lewis guns for the larger models. Lord Beaverbrook, as Minister for Aircraft Production, ordered an unwieldy armoured version of the six-wheel Leyland Retriever 3-ton lorry, nicknamed the Beaver-Eel, for the protection of aircraft factories, and these could carry a 20mm cannon with all-round traverse.

Imbued by the Prime Minister's rhetoric with the Dunkirk spirit, other companies and even individuals got in on the act. The London, Midland and Scottish Railway collected all the old lorries it could find and began a conversion programme that involved fitting to the back of each one a double thickness wooden box, insulated between the layers with a filling of pebbles which, rumour had it, would resist rifle fire. They were called Armadillos. Early models appeared on every kind of chassis imaginable and only carried light weapons, but in due course even this improvised fleet took on a degree of standardisation and, can it be said, sophistication. The Mark III version on new Bedford 3-ton chassis featured a smaller fighting box with another dug-out, the 1½ pounder COW gun of 1918, mounted at the back. Pillboxes were springing up all over the country and Concrete Ltd hit upon the idea of making them mobile too. Once again it was a matter of gathering up old lorries which were then stripped down and rebuilt with a covering of reinforced concrete that formed a cab at the front and pillbox at the back. With this kind of load mobility was clearly going to be a problem, but since they were intended only for airfield defence it was not thought to matter very much. The famous racing driver and world-record holder Sir Malcolm Campbell, and his chief mechanic Leo Villa, even fitted armour to a Fordson tractor, but this was felt to be going just a bit too far. For an encore they designed an armoured body for the Fordson lorry chassis which was constructed by a Ford subsidiary, Briggs Motor

Bodies Ltd. This resulted in a small production order for similar vehicles on a Dodge chassis.

Incongruous as some of these vehicles may have looked in comparison with frontline equipment, they were the epitome of professionalism when compared with the amazing collection of motorised deathtraps assembled by the Home Guard. Formed in May 1940 as the Local Defence Volunteers, this force grew, in days, to a size that rivalled that of the regular army. Although it has been the butt of much affectionate mirth, it took itself very seriously and fulfilled a useful role once it was organised properly. As its armoury grew from pikestaffs and shotguns to rifles and automatic weapons, so did its aspirations as a fighting force. This led members of some units to consider obtaining armoured vehicles, notwithstanding the desperate

29 Crowds in Aberdeen are suitably impressed by a Leyland Beaver-Eel of the Ministry of Aircraft Production. The armament of these vehicles varied but usually included a 1½-pounder COW gun. However this one seems only to be equipped with Vickers K machine-guns.

28 Bedford OXA armoured lorries under construction at Luton. No fixed armament was mounted, the crew simply fired small arms through the loopholes.

30 The LMS railway built the wooden bodied Armadillos at their Wolverton works. This over-protected specimen, a Mark II, used the Bedford OY chassis.

shortage of them everywhere else. The only option left open to them was to make their own, using donated cars which their owners had laid up for the duration on account of the fuel shortage. Design was individual to the point of eccentricity since it depended entirely on local theories and resources, and there appears to have been no constructive interchange of ideas between units. Officially the whole practice was frowned upon, if not actively discouraged, as most of the cars produced were masterpieces of bad design which offered their crews very little in the way of effective protection. A typical example was a 25hp Sunbeam which Colonel W M Tickler of the Maidenhead

31   There was really no such thing as a typical Bison, they were as individual as the chassis they ran on. Entry was usually through a trapdoor in the floor, which must have made them potential death traps. This one served at an airfield in the West Country.

32   The combined talents of Sir Malcolm Campbell and his engineer Leo Villa joined with the Ford Motor Company to produce this prototype armoured Fordson for home defence duties. Production models followed on a Dodge chassis.

(Berkshire) Battalion ordered to be built using the resources at the jam-making factory of which he was managing director. The chassis was fitted with a framework of angle iron, scrounged from a local scrapyard. To this was welded panels of quarter-inch thick plate surmounted by an open-topped turret. Two Vickers machine-guns were fitted, one in the turret and the other on its tripod, poking out the back, while a Bren gun could be fired through a slit alongside the driver. When it was reviewed in *The Motor* magazine in July 1940 it was hailed as a classic example of self-help, and it was suggested that plate should be supplied, already cut and drilled, from a central depot, to be fitted to any suitable car by a local garage. This was never done and in practice individuality was the rule. Most units which decided to build cars only ever had one or two and few could equal the Kings Lynn (Norfolk) Battalion which operated a fleet of seven. It would require a separate volume to catalogue and describe all those cars of which records survive so the accompanying illustrations have been chosen to serve the purpose instead. It should be noted that later on, when the immediate fear of invasion subsided, the Home Guard reverted to other roles, notably rounding up surviving enemy aircrew and as a back-up to the Civil Defence authorities. Officialdom also relented to some extent on the subject of armoured cars and Standard Beaverettes were issued for patrol work.

Not to be outdone, the Royal Artillery joined in this orgy of motorised madness under the guise of coastal defence. Redundant 4-inch guns were borrowed from the Admiralty and mounted on heavy lorries – which were also partly armoured – and stationed in potential invasion areas. They were formidable-looking vehicles, quite capable of sinking a landing craft if the occasion presented itself (and the chassis withstood the shock). Smaller weapons, Hotchkiss 3-pounders and 3-inch (12-pounder)

33   An AEC Mammoth 6×4 truck acts as the mount for a 4-inch QF Mark 4 gun, an ex-Naval weapon. Foden and Mammoth Major chassis were also employed.

coastal defence guns also appeared on lighter chassis, but none seem to have survived the invasion scare.

The vulnerability of the royal family and senior Cabinet ministers, both to air raids and surprise paratroop attacks, gave rise to some concern. This resulted in the formation of the Morris Mission, under Lieutenant W A Morris, in June 1940. Initially it acted simply as an escort service using three rather ancient armoured cars, but by September these had been exchanged for Guys. The objects of their care, the King, Queen and Prime Minister, were expected to give up the stylish comfort of their Daimlers for modified versions of the Humberette. Known as Special Ironside Saloons they appeared in two types – the earlier pattern with no windows – which were fully enclosed and finished inside to Pullman standards by the coachbuilders Thrupp and Maberley, but they were unwieldy and claustrophobic for all that. Crews were selected from the 12th Lancers, while the escorting armoured cars were manned by the Royal Northamptonshire Yeomanry. Yet for obvious reasons both the King and Queen preferred to be seen during their travels, especially in the capital, so before long conventional Humber Pullman saloons were provided with more discreet armour protection and bullet-proof glass.

The effect of the invasion threat on the Royal Armoured Corps was considerable. It was hopeless to start thinking of expansion before existing regiments had been re-equipped, and even as production got into its stride, under the additional threat of air attack it was necessary to improvise. Those divisional cavalry regiments that formed the two Armoured Reconnaissance Brigades in France, along with the six regiments earmarked for 3rd Armoured Division and 25th Army Tank Brigade, were temporarily reconstituted as one Light Armoured Reconnaissance Brigade and three Motor Machine Gun Brigades equipped with the various vintage and improvised AFVs recorded above. The erstwhile 20th Armoured Brigade formed, for a while, the Yeomanry Armoured Detachment equipped with carriers and Guy armoured cars on a two to one basis. As they were smarting still from the experience in France, and convinced of the vulnerability of open-topped vehicles to air attack, the decision was taken to fit the carriers with armoured roofs. Although it did not seriously affect performance the low roof made it very difficult for the crew to disembark in an emergency. By the end of the year, as the immediate threat diminished and stocks of tanks and armoured cars increased, most of these units reverted to their original organisations and roles. In November there was an increase in the number of armoured regiments with the creation of four new Royal Tank Regiments and three cavalry, plus one more in January 1941.

Even as the events of May and June were being digested, and the qualities of current British AFVs evaluated, further developments were taking place. New models of the Daimler scout car appeared without the

34 HM Queen Elizabeth—our present Queen Mother—steps out of her Humber Special Ironside armoured car. Despite a high standard of internal comfort it must have been claustrophobic inside and did not allow the Royal Family to maintain the high profile they wished to present in public.

35 Carriers of the Yeomanry Armoured Detachment on patrol. A Scout Carrier leads but the nearest vehicle is a Universal, fitted with the awkward armoured roof.

troublesome four-wheel steering and with the original sliding roof changed for a folding one. In fact these were so rarely used that before long a roof of any kind was dispensed with in favour of a canvas cover. Early models were returned to workshops to have the rear-axle steering disconnected and welded up. From the Mark IB onwards the airflow across the radiator was reversed, resulting in a slight alteration to the shape of the rear end. Meanwhile Daimler was working on another BSA design for a proper armoured car based upon the structural and mechanical features of the scout car. These included a similarly shaped body with rear-engine layout. A more powerful 95hp engine was employed, linked by fluid flywheel to a preselector gearbox and by separate shafts to each of the four individually sprung wheels. But the real revolution, as far as Britain was concerned, lay in the armament. Although originally specified to carry a typical twin machine-gun mounting, the turret, which was similar to that designed for the Vickers-Armstrong Mark VII light tank,

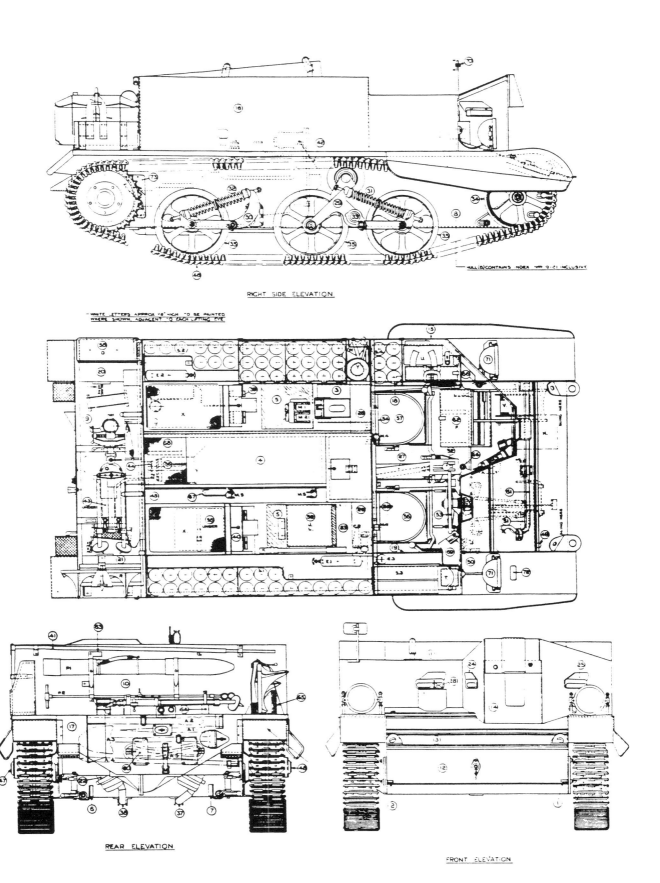

RIGHT SIDE ELEVATION

REAR ELEVATION

FRONT ELEVATION

Drawing G: A Universal Carrier shown here stowed to carry a 3-inch mortar and ammunition.

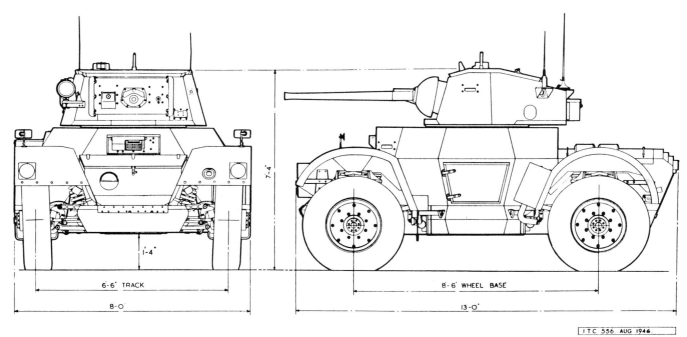

Main dimensions of Armoured-Car, Daimler

ITC 556 AUG 1946

Drawing H: Front and side views of a Daimler Mark I Armoured Car.

36 *A Daimler Mark I armoured car on the company test ground. This angle provides a good view of the tough independent suspension.*

was ultimately equipped with a 2-pounder gun and coaxial Besa. The result was that for the first time an armoured car was available with a respectable armament: indeed, at the time of its introduction it was as powerfully armed as any current British service tank. It had even been planned that the car should have four-wheel steering, but this was dropped following experience with the scout cars, although a duplicate steering-wheel was fitted, facing backwards, by means of which a crew member could quickly take over and reverse the car out of trouble. Following gunnery trials at Lulworth one of the prototypes

was loaned to 20th Armoured Brigade for advanced user trials which produced favourable comments.

The demand for increased production of armoured cars caused problems for Guy Motors above and beyond those already posed by the many faults that had been revealed. The company was already committed to an increased output of trucks and field artillery tractors, as well as buses for the civilian market, so it was decided to switch armoured-car production to the Karrier Company in the Rootes Group. This firm already had a suitable four-wheel drive chassis in production as an artillery tractor for the Indian Army, the model KT4 powered by a 90hp six-cylinder engine. It was readily modified to rear-engine configuration to accept the Guy-built armoured hulls, but to avoid any confusion that use of the trade name Karrier might create in service it was officially classified as Humber. The Mark I was, with some detail differences, virtually identical to the Guy Mark IA, and indeed the first batch of 140 hulls had similar faults in the armour plate, but from the Mark II onwards a revised hull designed and built within the Rootes Group was produced. This had an improved driver's cab arrangement which simplified production and even provided a bit more room, and a device that raised the engine cover hydraulically so that the driver had a better view when reversing.

The success of the Bren and Scout Carriers, when they were not trying to be tanks, had been established in France. Yet even before then it had been appreciated that there was really no need to build such diverse types for what were very similar roles. Early in 1939 a design had been worked out for a multipurpose model that became

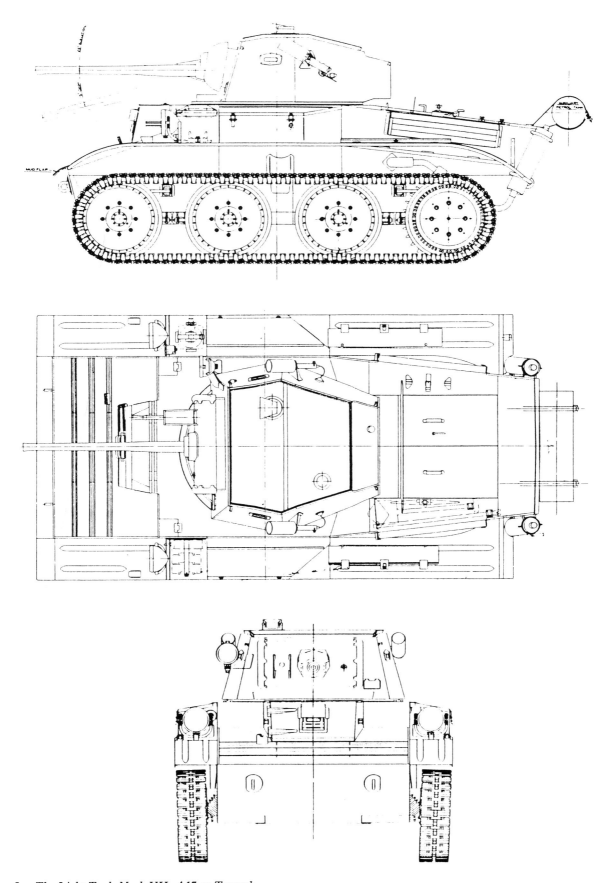

Drawing I: The Light Tank Mark VII, A17 or Tetrarch.

known as the Universal Carrier. It was in fullscale production by 1940 with a host of manufacturers and differed from the older models mainly in the design of the rear hull which featured full-length compartments on both sides of the engine. Initially there were two basic versions: the definitive Universal was adaptable to cavalry and infantry requirements, while a special Armoured Observation Post model had been developed for the Royal Artillery. Some time later another version equipped to transport a 3-inch mortar and crew appeared, and over the next few years the variations and variety of uses to which they were put seemed almost endless. Soon the demand was such that an 85hp version of the Ford V8 engine was being imported from the United States to supplement supplies of the 65hp British model. Three Commonwealth countries, most notably Canada, also became producers of complete vehicles.

Captain Vivian Loyd, the survivor of the old Carden-Loyd partnership, offered a carrier of his own design to the War Office in 1939, and formed a company to produce it. The Loyd Carrier also used Ford components; the chassis, engine, gearbox and rear axle of their 2-ton truck, as the basis for a simple – some might say crude – 1-ton load carrier. By placing the engine at the back, inverting the driving axle and fitting it at the front, Loyd achieved the desired result of maximum capacity for transporting either personnel or stores. The tracks and suspension were derived from the Vickers carrier although its complicated steering system was not adopted. The majority of these vehicles were unarmoured and no provision was made for mounting weapons, except in some later experimental models. The roles selected for the Loyd were numerous – as well as those mentioned above they served as anti-tank gun tractors, signal-line layers and slave battery vehicles. Armoured units in particular employed this last type as the Carrier, Tracked, Starting and Charging, which carried a bank of batteries down each side and the necessary power take-off and dynamo to recharge them. However, in this as in many other roles the vehicle was seriously overloaded, and suffered for it.

Despite a massive expansion in production facilities throughout the United Kingdom – and before long overseas as well – Vickers-Armstrong Ltd continued to play a significant part in British tank development in the first two years of the war. All the same it is worth noting that during the war they studiously avoided any involvement in the production of rival designs. There was a feeling in some quarters that they exercised an undue influence over the deliberations of the Tank Board even before one of their own senior staff members (Commander Sir Robert Micklem RN) headed it, but since this opinion was only ever expressed openly by Sir Albert Stern it is worth treating with some caution. There is, of course, no doubt that apart from the official Department of Tank Design Vickers was the greatest single repository of experience on the subject in Britain, and there were times when

this might have been used to some effect. Firm in this knowledge Vickers adopted a policy of independence, which may gradually have alienated them from user experience and requirements, although it should not be forgotten that tanks were only one part of their total stock-in-trade for all three armed services.

Vickers had two tank designs on offer at the outbreak of war, both of which had originated as private ventures, albeit with a view to War Office custom. Thus, although neither began life with the blessing of a General Staff requirement the army was obliged, of necessity, to take an interest in them. The first was a light tank that had been designed speculatively before the war and been accepted – under the GS specification A17 – in 1938. This later became known as the Tetrarch. Experience in France had since proved that even a light tank needed to carry something heavier than machine-guns if it was to live up to its name, and A17 mounted the 2-pounder. Indeed, with this armament and a 14mm armour standard it was almost on a par with A9 and A13, so at one stage there was a move to reclassify it as a light cruiser. In order to keep the tank as compact as possible a flat, horizontally opposed twelve-cylinder engine by Henry Meadows Ltd, the model MAT, was adopted which, driving through a five-speed gearbox, gave the 7.5 ton tank an admirable top speed of 40 mph on the road. Its performance was further enhanced by an ingenious suspension and steering system. Instead of the Horstmann coilsprings that Vickers had used on all their previous light tanks the Tetrarch ran on four large-diameter roadwheels at each side, which supported the hull on hydro-pneumatic struts. Large-radius turns were achieved with a steering wheel which both tilted and turned the roadwheels in a complex piece of geometry and forced the tracks to adopt a curved configuration in relation to the ground. The effect of this was to avoid the age-old problem of skid turns, inherent in most tracked vehicles, which absorbed an inordinate amount of power and set up tremendous lateral stress in both tracks and suspension. On the other hand it required a lot of effort to operate and could only be used for turning-circles of 94ft diameter or more. Skid steering, with a lever-operated braked differential, had to be employed for tighter turns. Light Tank Mark VII, as the Tetrarch was also known, was originally ordered from Vickers-Armstrong's Elswick works but was transferred to Metro-Cammell in the summer of 1940. Production was slowed in the first place by serious problems with the engine cooling system, but just as this was resolved and before more than twenty tanks had been completed, the factory suffered badly from enemy bombing, and the Tank Board monthly production report for May 1941 stressed that further deliveries could not be expected in the near future.

How the Valentine got its name is still the subject of divided opinions, most of them Kiplingesque, although one may hold a kernel of truth – that it was because the

37   *Captain Loyd's simple but effective Carrier viewed from overhead by the official photographer at Kidbrooke depot.*

tank was offered to the War Office on St Valentine's Day 1938. It wasn't, but it was only a day or two short of that date. Another claims that it was chosen as a tribute to Sir John Carden – it was his middle name – since he was responsible for the design of its suspension; but Carden had been dead for three years by this time. The third is only worthy of a dedicated crossword addict and is based on the theory that it is an acronym of *Vickers-Armstrong Ltd, Elswick & Newcastle-upon-TINE (sic)*, which takes a bit of swallowing. At its most prosaic it is clearly a codeword of the sort many large engineering firms used as an in-house identifier for their products, and it may have no more significance to it than that. After all, the codeword Matilda was chosen for the Infantry Tank Mark I (another Vickers product) when the original specification was drawn up; it had nothing to do with Sir Hugh Elles's claim that he nicknamed it after a certain comic duck when he saw the prototype waddling along.

However it may be, a precedent for naming tanks had been set as long ago as 1917 when the Medium A was nicknamed Whippet and a year later the Medium C became Hornet. It is a peculiarly British trait that fell into abeyance between the wars, to anthropomorphise machines. Its revival is attributed to Winston Churchill. Tank nomenclature was getting complicated; the original General Staff designation was being modified to cover developments in such a way that the A13, for instance, now appeared in four guises, A13 Mk I, Mk II, Mk IIA and Mark III, and other examples could be shown. In a letter dated 11 June 1940 – as if they had nothing more important to do – the Army Council announced that in future, to avoid confusion (!) tanks would be described by function and mark alone; eg Tank, Infantry Mark II; Tank, Cruiser Mark IV etc. That was simple enough – too simple for some – but it failed to take other variations into account, so qualifications were introduced. The suffix

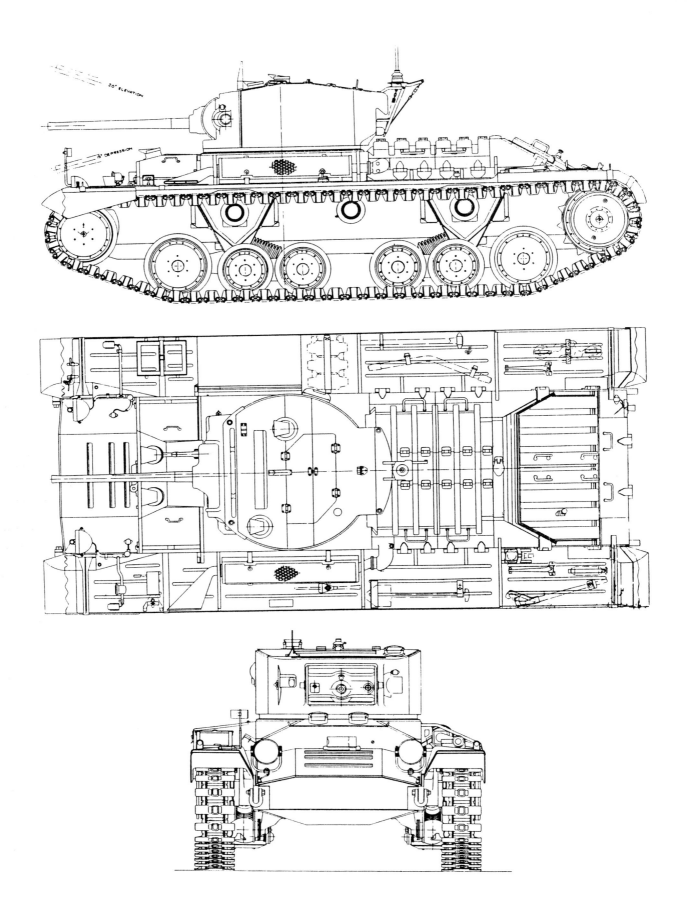

Drawing J: Infantry Tank Mark III, Valentine with the original two-man turret.

A signified a change in armament while an asterisk indicated a different type of engine. Thus the Infantry Mark II carried AEC engines and a coaxial Vickers gun while the Mark IIA* had Leyland engines and a Besa. To complicate matters still further those tanks fitted with a 3-inch howitzer should have the letters CS added to their title for Close Support. Ideal as they might be for civil servants, such designations looked more like algebraic formulae to the Prime Minister, who also felt that they lacked the public appeal of stirring names. It was a matter upon which the Royal Navy and Royal Air Force had the edge, so a further change was ordained. Who exactly chose the names remains a mystery, and the fact that most began with the third letter of the alphabet seems, initially at least, to have been fortuitous.

Even so the earlier designations were retained officially and names were not issued retrospectively so that the Cruiser Mark I, as it should have been called, was always known as the A9. The Valentine was also the Infantry Mark III, although this basic model ran to eleven variants, so its full title should read; Tank, Infantry Mark III, Valentine I, or V, as appropriate. They began to enter service in July 1940 – but this might never have been.

Valentine, like the Tetrarch, was a speculative design, but not such an original one since it was based on the more successful features of the A10 heavy cruiser. Indeed, one of these tanks had been ballasted to 16 tons (some 3 tons over its designed battle weight) in order to prove that the suspension was up to it. What damned the new tank in War Office eyes was the two-man turret which conflicted with the longstanding requirement that a turret crew of three was essential to free the commander from any specific duties involved in working the gun. Vickers had designed an automatic 40mm (2-pounder) gun with a performance that came close to the official War Office weapon and this would have been more suitable for a two-man turret, but it was never specified for Valentine, presumably because the tank was intended from the start to suit British requirements.

Since most of the mechanical components were already proven on the A10, production began without the need to build pilot models. In this case it was justified although, as the next chapter shows, other attempts to bypass the system had disastrous results. There were teething troubles, notably with the tracks before an effective type was developed, but generally the tank performed very well indeed. Due in part to the small turret it was a compact design, of riveted construction with a maximum armour thickness of 65mm. The driver sat centrally at the front, there was no provision for a hull machine-gun or gunner, and the turret mounted a Besa alongside the 2-pounder. The first model used an AEC petrol engine and Vickers rejected any of the more complex transmission systems then on offer in favour of a conventional gearbox with clutch and brake steering. The Valentine's career is so bound up with the desert war that further comment is

reserved for Chapter 5, but for the present it should be explained that the design was neither one thing nor the other. It was lightly armoured for an infantry tank, even by 1940 standards, but rather on the slow side for a cruiser, managing only half the speed (15 mph) of an A13, for instance. It made up for both shortcomings with the virtue of reliability and subsequently served in large numbers in both roles, although it never had the distinction, such as it was, of carrying a GS specification number, no doubt because of its unofficial origins.

There were many other types of armoured vehicle that appeared in the first years of the war which fall outside the mainstream of AFV development but which nevertheless deserve a brief mention. Many of them never saw service, active or otherwise, and few did anything to enhance Britain's reputation as a designer of military vehicles, although they all serve to illustrate certain trends in tactical thought and design. When the BEF went to France in 1939 a number of divisions included one battalion equipped with motorcycle machine-gun units which served in the divisional reconnaissance role. The idea had been tried, with very little success, in the First World War, and one wonders why it was revived, because under active service conditions the new types proved just as vulnerable. When he returned from France Vyvyan Pope suggested that they ought to be replaced by light armoured vehicles. The Daimler scout car would appear to have been the ideal choice, but for some unexplained reason Pope encouraged other firms to design and build even simpler vehicles. Morris Motors led the way with a tiny one-man machine which mounted two forward-firing machine-guns. They were fixed rigidly into the body on each side of the car so that the driver had to aim the vehicle itself before firing them, rather as a fighter pilot would with his plane. Another Morris design was the Salamander. It carried a crew of two in a slim armoured body surmounted by a tiny open-top turret mounting a

38 Two Morris products of the emergency period. On the left a Light Reconnaissance Car Mark I, a three-man type which saw considerable service. On the right the one-man variant, the Glanville Fighter Car with its two fixed machine-guns, which did not enter service at all.

Bren gun. The driver sat centrally at the front with the gunner above and behind him with his head in the turret. The Hillman Company followed with the very similar Gnat which used chassis components from their 10hp Light Utility Truck. None of these vehicles had four-wheel drive. The whole project was dropped quickly following Pope's departure for the Middle East and subsequent death, but enthusiasm was so strong at one time that Morris produced a drawing to show how their cars would deal with inland water obstacles. Each car towed a pair of pontoon-style floats on two wheels as a small trailer until it reached a river. Here the crew attached the floats to the sides of the car and launched themselves upon the waters.

Earlier still, in 1939, Guy Motors came up with the design of what was in effect a wheeled version of the Universal Carrier. It was based on their four-wheel drive armoured-car chassis, but when the mild steel prototype was delivered to the Mechanisation Experimental Establishment in June 1940, it was found to be riddled with major and minor defects. Estimates showed that the amount of work required to put all these right was so great that the project was dropped and the machine returned to the makers.

One of the most bizarre military vehicles of all time was developed from an idea put forward by a Mr E J Tapp of the County Commercial Company, although that firm was not formally registered until after the war. Tapp set out to achieve a vehicle with the lowest possible silhouette yet capable of firing from behind obstacles of any reasonable height. The first of these was rendered possible by having the crewman adopt a prone position, face downwards, in

39 Morris Motors also produced the two-man Salamander to replace motorcycle sidecar units of recce regiments. Like its rival, the Hillman Gnat, the Salamander was never adopted.

41 Mr Tapp's original one-man Praying Mantis at full elevation. The crewman, in the metal box, would almost be standing upright at this stage.

40 A Guy Motors publicity picture compares their prototype wheeled carrier with a tracked Universal built, in this instance, by Nuffields.

a sort of steel box, slung between the track frames. This entire box was capable of being elevated until it was almost vertical while the weapon, a light machine-gun, was contained within a sort of gimbal-mounted hood which formed the forward extremity of the box. The suspension was derived from the Carden-Loyd system and the engine was mounted at the back, close by the trunnions upon which the crew box elevated. The crewman could drive the vehicle and fire the gun from any position between horizontal and maximum elevation. In the former position the entire vehicle only came up to the knee of a standing infantryman and it could scurry about using small bushes and even tall grass for cover. It could conceal itself behind the least cover and then poke its head up to spy out the country or fire its gun as necessary. The hood allowed sufficient movement to elevate or depress the gun and permit it to swing, to a limited extent, left and right of the centre line. It must have been the most uncomfortable thing to travel in and quite a handful for one man, who not only had to drive and fire the gun but also control the elevating apparatus for that part of the vehicle which he occupied. There is no doubt that it was an exceedingly odd machine and one wonders if anyone with any military experience had really given very much thought to how it might be employed. Even so the concept obviously tickled a bevy of generals who saw it demonstrated at Sandhurst shortly after the outbreak of war; it must still have been the silly season. Their main objection was the same that the War Office had levelled against Carden and Martel; that a one-man operated fighting-vehicle demanded too much of its crew. However, they encouraged Tapp to design a two-man machine and the plans for this were ready by the end of the year.

At the War Office more sober heads prevailed and a series of delays kept the design on ice until 1943, when the new prototype finally appeared. This was based on Universal Carrier components as far as the suspension, tracks and Ford V8 engine were concerned but the fighting chamber was wider, since two men now occupied it side by side and even in repose it was somewhat higher than the first version. The vision hood was still capable of elevation and depression but the armament, a pair of Bren guns, was fitted upside down in a small, coffin-shaped box on top of the hood. The guns had to be inverted so that the gunner could fit new magazines from below but the box they were in could be elevated and rotated independently to give a much wider field of fire. Coffin was not an inappropriate word to describe the whole machine. When shared by two men it must have been claustrophobic in the extreme, but for one man, in action, it would have been a severe test of morale. The new vehicle acquired the nickname Praying Mantis on account of its strange appearance, but it had little else to commend it except novelty value and was finally rejected, following trials, in the summer of 1944.

As the next chapter shows, the plan to replace the

42 *Firefly was a Morris Light Reconnaissance Car modified to carry a 6-pounder anti-tank gun. It was a tight fit and a very unsatisfactory combination which was rejected for service.*

43 *When Humber fitted a 6-pounder into a turretless version of their armoured car there was a bit more room, but it resulted in a singularly ugly vehicle.*

obsolete 2-pounder gun with a 6-pounder in tanks did not run smoothly, and the guns were available long before any tanks were ready to accept them. A number of ideas were put forward, as a consequence, and two quite interesting ones never got beyond the prototype stage. They were proposed by Humber and Morris, the former basing theirs on the design of their existing armoured car. Morris Motors tried to shoehorn the weapon into a modified version of their Light Reconnaissance Car. There was precious little room to spare inside either of these vehicles at the best of times and the installation of the 6-pounder must have been crippling, not to mention its effect on the handling of the vehicle. Humber installed the gun fairly high up, in a turretless version of their armoured car, but Morris, who called theirs the Firefly, set it low down in the front of the hull, projecting well ahead of the vehicle. Neither had the chance to stand the test of active service, being abandoned at the prototype stage.

It will be recalled how both Guy Motors and, later, Karrier (Humber) had developed practical armoured cars

44 *An AEC Mark I armoured car at a depot in the Middle East. Compare the 2-pounder turret with a Valentine Mark I, they should be the same.*

by utilising the chassis of their respective field artillery tractors. In 1940 AEC of Southall attempted the same thing with the chassis of their highly successful medium artillery tractor, the Matador. It was a large, diesel-engined four-wheel drive truck, the chassis frame of which was modified by dropping the centre section and moving the engine to the rear. A high-sided but narrow armoured hull was then fitted, surmounted by a Valentine tank turret containing a 2-pounder gun. With armour to a maximum of 30mm it was well protected for an armoured car but high – over eight feet – and heavy at eleven tons, although it still retained a fair turn of speed. Bearing in mind that a senior member of the AEC staff was also connected with the Directorate of Tank Design it is odd to discover that their armoured car appears to have been built as a speculative project, with no official sanction whatever. Certainly there is no record of a General Staff specification although in some respects it came closer to the idea, conceived later in the war, of what an armoured car ought to be. Since the project had to be sold to the War Office the company took the highly irregular step of inserting the prototype, unofficially, into a display of British armoured vehicles held on Horse Guards Parade in

1941. For this event it was brightly painted and, as calculated, caught the attention of Winston Churchill whose interest was sufficient to guarantee an initial order for 122 cars which was placed in June. Even so production was delayed by a shortage of turrets, which could only be obtained from Valentine tanks, which were being converted into bridgelayers. It was thus well into 1942 before they began to appear with service units in North Africa.

The Matador chassis also served as the basis for a highly specialised, and in this case highly successful, piece of equipment, the Armoured Command Vehicle (ACV). It has already been mentioned in passing that some of the original Morris light armoured-car chassis had been diverted to this purpose when they entered production in 1938 but the type was cramped, and lacked four-wheel drive. The role of the ACV was to provide a mobile command post for senior officers, which enabled them to keep in close touch with units in the field behind a modest amount of armour protection. The Morris version saw service in North Africa although an unidentified prototype had accompanied the BEF to France. This, by all accounts, proved very useful although legend has it that the protection offered was no more than painted plywood.

The Morris was followed into production by a four-wheel drive type which used the Guy Lizard chassis and some of these, too, served in the Middle East, but only a small number were produced, and production ended when the firm abandoned armoured-vehicle construction to concentrate on trucks. The Lizard was also rather cramped inside although the chassis was better suited to the payload which, in addition to the armour, included wireless sets capable of maintaining contact with both tanks and rear headquarters.

The AEC design dates from a General Staff specification issued early in 1940 which, in fact, covered a family of vehicles. These were an Armoured Mine Layer (AML), Armoured Demolition Vehicle (ADV), Armoured Personnel Carrier (APC), and the ACV. Orders were placed for small quantities of each with AEC and Weyman Motor Bodies, who would assemble the hulls. The object was to equip 1st Armoured Division with its establishment of mild-steel prototypes in the first instance for evaluation. All four variants had similar fully-enclosed bodies adapted as necessary to each role. The AML carried a large quantity of anti-tank mines which it deposited through a chute as it went along. The ADV mounted a compressor, rock drill and pile driver which operated through openings cut in the floor and roof. This would enable a Royal Engineers demolition team to work on bridges and similar structures from the relative safety of an armoured vehicle without, in theory, ever having to dismount. The APC would simply carry parties of infantry into action alongside armoured vehicles, but in the event it seems that this version was never proceeded with, and during the design stage they were converted to ACVs. A similar fate befell the AMLs. A change in policy required that anti-tank mines be buried rather than dropped straight on to the ground, so the chute and feed equipment was removed and the vehicles redesignated Armoured Mine Carriers (AMC). It was an expensive way of carrying mines about, so in due course this project was also dropped and the vehicles altered to the ACV specification. The fate of the demolition version is not so clear. A report dated April 1941 suggests that they entered production, but if so they were never mentioned again and the chances are that the end result was even more ACVs. The ACV version itself, by contrast, went from strength to strength. Two versions, with high power (HP) and low power (LP) communications equipment, were produced and they proved very popular, especially in the desert where the enemy could approach quite suddenly from any direction. Indeed three AECs, captured by the Germans, were used by General Crüwell and General Rommel, who preferred them to their own cramped half-tracks.

45   *A camouflaged Guy Lizard armoured command vehicle in the desert with penthouse erected at the side. The staff officer in the foreground poses for the photographer and pretends to look at his map.*

46   *An AEC Dorchester armoured command vehicle in the Middle East. Probably named after the hotel, rather than the town it was one of the least shapely armoured vehicles ever built.*

SF1 *The best equipped Home Guard unit in the country was undoubtedly the Kings Lynn Battalion in Norfolk. They ran a fleet of at least seven cars which are shown here. Numbering from the left they are: a 1934 20hp Alvis, 1937 30hp Ford, 1935 30hp Ford, 1934 16hp Hillman, 1935 16hp Hillman, 1934 16hp Rover and, for the commander, a 1936 29hp Straight Eight Railton reputedly capable of 90 mph. Four of the cars bear the insignia of 2nd Corps.*

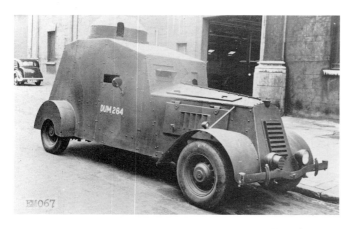

SF2 *Built by the Ford subsidiary Briggs Motor Bodies of Dagenham on a Wolseley chassis, this very professional effort served with the Beccles, Suffolk Home Guard.*

SF4 *The LCC Battalion also operated this well designed 1936 Standard which is seen taking part in another rather one-sided mock battle.*

SF3 *Members of the Kemsley House* (Daily Sketch) *Home Guard are introduced to an armoured Rolls-Royce of the London County Council (County of London) Battalion after it had defeated them in a mock battle. The car, a 1930 model 40/50, was donated by the chairman of the LCC.*

SF5 *The London Passenger Transport Board built 20 of these ponderous vehicles at their Chiswick depot for their Home Guard Battalion. AEC Regent (ST) double-decker bus chassis were used, which staggered along beneath an all-up load of 12 tons.*

SF6   *Brigadier General Wade Haynes of the 1st American (Eagle) Squadron, Home Guard introduces his armoured car to the Prime Minister in January 1941. Strictly speaking neutral Americans were not eligible to serve with the Home Guard at all.*

SF7   *Camelford, in Cornwall brought out its armoured car to take part in a War Weapons Week parade.*

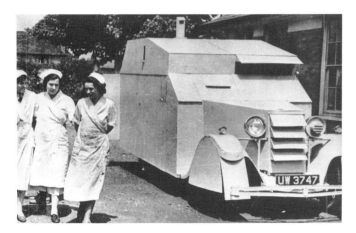

SF8   *Colonel Tickler's first design for the Maidenhead Battalion appears to overpower the 1936, 25hp Sunbeam chassis. Presumably the ladies work in the Colonel's jam factory.*

SF9   *In its second form the Maidenhead Sunbeam was altogether more recognisable as a car, and now sported a turret.*

SF10   *The ultimate version of the Tickler Sunbeam carried a Vickers gun in an open top turret and another, on its tripod, in the back.*

SF11   *This big Hudson Terraplane also belonged to the Maidenhead Home Guard and was another of Tickler's designs. It was a much less drastic conversion with a Vickers machine-gun mounted to fire through the sunshine roof.*

SF12 *Fitting the windscreen armour to a Ford sedan of the Maidenhead Battalion. The box which protects the radiator is filled with small stones.*

SF13 *In Kent the 53rd (Orpington & Swanley) Battalion built this armoured car on a Rolls-Royce chassis using scrap materials salvaged from a gravel pit. It was designed with the unnerving ability to slam the driver's visor shut when the brakes were applied hard.*

SF14 *The very essence of the Home Guard is summed up by this picture of a long suffering old Buick. Its owner, in the cap, is a retired Guardsman, 2nd Lieutenant Oxley, of the West Farleigh (Kent) Battalion.*

SF15 At Arundel in Sussex they painted their car with trees in the hope that it would blend in with the background.

SF16 Tubby Tankbuster was a Malcolm Campbell Dodge armoured car cut down and fitted with the 6-pounder gun from a First World War tank. It belonged to a Home Guard Battalion at Somerford, near Christchurch in Hampshire.

SF17 Minehead in Somerset was the home of this unidentified car. They also operated an old Morris Cowley pick-up truck with a Vickers gun in the back.

SF18 The 7th Battalion, Gloucestershire Home Guard, based at Stroud, had two armoured cars, Daniel and The Eagle, based on 30hp Austin chassis. They were donated by a Mr A H Radcliffe and covered in 3/8 inch plate by Daniels of Stroud. Their other vehicle was an ambulance called Echo which was a modified Austin hearse!

SF19 A Thornycroft lorry was converted into a fair representation of a Rolls-Royce armoured car by the 16th (City of Bristol) Battalion. Their other vehicle was a lorry carrying a spigot mortar.

SF20 Mrs John Appleton of Stevenage offered her Bentley for conversion by the 3rd Hertfordshire Battalion. It mounts a Lewis gun on an aircraft type Scarfe ring. Mr Appleton is standing beside the car.

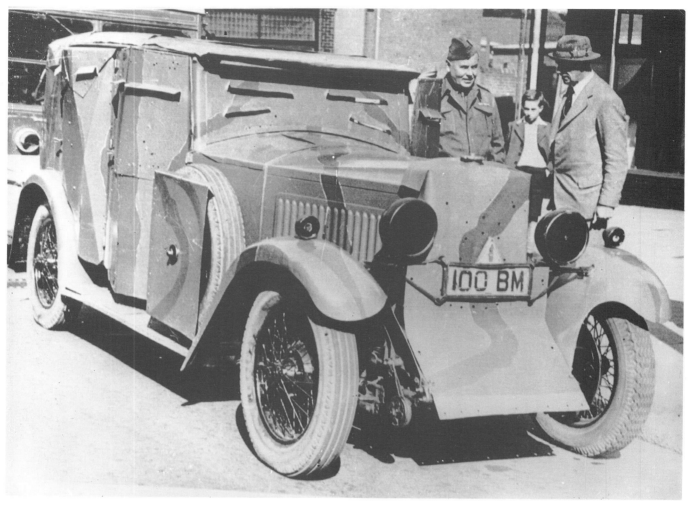

SF21 *Only a Vauxhall would do for Luton in Bedfordshire. It was a 20/60 saloon presented by Mr C R Thompson and given a rather rough and ready conversion.*

SF22 *This car, believed to be a Wolseley, served with the Northamptonshire Home Guard at Wellingborough.*

SF23 *A local engineering firm in Stockport built this rather spartan car from Austin and Riley parts for the Cheshire Home Guard. It is armed with a Browning Automatic Rifle.*

SF24 *Another mystery car, but a well designed one, which is believed to have served with a Cheshire Home Guard unit based at Sandiway. The conversion is said to have cost £80.*

SF26 *An unidentified unit in Lancashire went in for the sporty look with their 35hp Chrysler. Not only does it mount two stripped Lewis guns it carries a crew of six, is said to have been fitted with wireless and tows a 2-pounder anti-tank gun.*

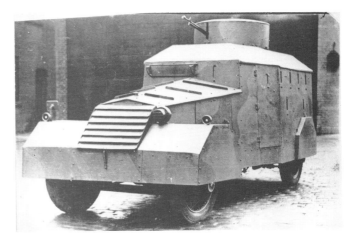

SF25 *Although this car is identified as a Sunbeam from Yorkshire its actual home-base is not known. It is seen taking part in an exercise and about to be on the receiving end of a Molotov cocktail.*

SF27 *The bus garage at Burnley produced this big armoured car on a Rolls-Royce chassis for the 29th Battalion, East Lancashire Home Guard. The car, which was described as a 20 year old hearse, was covered in ¼ inch plate, mounted a stripped Lewis gun in the turret and had seats for six men.*

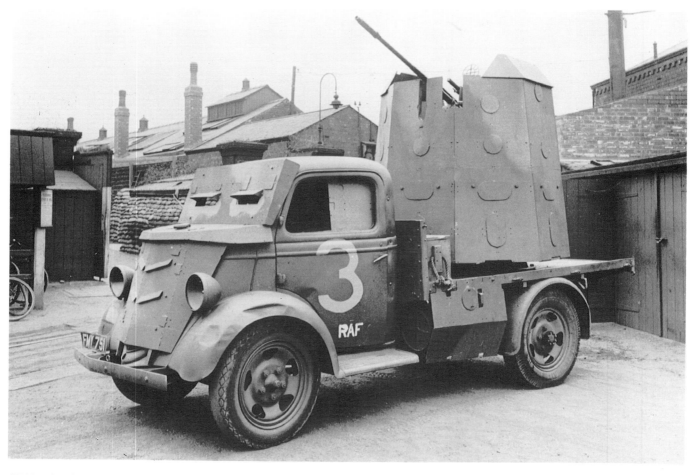

SF29   Another LNER product from Doncaster was this armoured Fordson for the Royal Air Force. The gun is mounted in a
Dalek-like turret at the back.

SF28   The Doncaster works of the London and North Eastern
Railway built this heavily protected lorry on what is believed to
be a Dennis chassis.

SF30   Flossie was a Bedford, but where she served and who built
her is not recorded.

4 Unbattleworthy

47 *Churchill tanks of 148 RAC on manoeuvres; in the foreground a Mark I with the hull-mounted howitzer, Mark IIs behind and a few Mark IIIs can be seen among those on the skyline.*

Even as the Nazi subjugation of Western Europe was making headlines all round the world and the climactic invasion of the British Isles was expected hourly, the machinery of daily life in Britain was ticking steadily away. In the tank factories work continued as usual, albeit on a round-the-clock basis. Nuffields in Birmingham were putting the finishing touches to the last Mark IV cruisers while Vickers-Armstrong's production line for the discredited All Infantry Tank still had two months to run. Indeed the last of these palpably useless machines would not be finished until 2 August. The same firm was gearing up to produce Valentines in large numbers while in other plants around the country work went on feverishly to produce as many Matildas and Tetrarchs as possible for a rapidly expanding army.

Other, newer designs, like Covenanter and Crusader, were in the experimental stage, but there was little likelihood of either actually being ready for service before the new year and in the meantime the country would have to manage as best it could. If production was to be expanded then it could only be done by drawing in more engineering firms with spare capacity, and if there were any such firms in June 1940 then the chances were that there was probably something seriously wrong with them.

That this was not always the case can be shown by a look at Vauxhall Motors. It will be recalled how a pilot model of the heavy A20 tank had been sent to their Luton factory to be fitted with the new Bedford twelve-cylinder horizontally opposed engine, but that the entire project was abandoned before any further work could be done.

In the same month a revised specification, A22, was submitted to the Defence Committee for a tank which was to become the Infantry Tank Mark IV. Owing, no doubt, to the prompt and efficient way that Vauxhall had carried out the work on the new engine it was suggested that they should continue with the new tank; undertake the detailed design and then act as parents to a group of companies charged with its production. In fact, of course, tank design is a highly specialised science which could not be left entirely to a commercial firm which normally manufactured motor cars, no matter what some of the company's later publicity might have implied. During the initial stages a team from the Department of Tank Design at Woolwich went up to Luton to work alongside the Vauxhall engineers. Designed broadly to the same specifications as the A20, on a slightly smaller scale, the new tank was to be 10 ft 8 ins long, to weigh 38.5 tons and carry 102mm thick armour, making it at the time one of the most heavily protected tanks yet built. Again, like the A20, it would carry a hull-mounted 3-inch howitzer at the front with the inevitable 2-pounder and coaxial Besa in the turret, although from the start it was agreed that a 6-pounder should be fitted as soon as that gun was available.

The Prime Minister took a special interest in this tank which in due course was to bear his name, but it was a mixed blessing. When the first order was placed on 1 July 1940 he demanded that 500 should be completed by March of the following year, despite a warning from the Director of Tanks and Transport that this was quite impossible, since nine months was just half the usual time required to produce the prototype of a brand new tank from the drawing board. In an attempt to satisfy this urge for haste it was decided to go straight into production from the drawing board. This bypassed the normal practice of building and thoroughly testing prototypes first. Such a course, which is anathema to any respectable engineer, could only be justified by the circumstances, and one engineer, when told that there would be no prototypes said that on the contrary there would be 500 of them! Yet the risks were accepted because, as the Prime Minister pointed out, with invasion imminent even immobilised tanks could be used as pillboxes in an emergency. The designers drew some comfort from the fact that the new tank would be using the Bedford flat-twelve engine and Merritt-Brown transmission selected for the A20, ignoring the point that this machine had only undergone the most rudimentary trials.

Never before can a new tank have had such inauspicious beginnings. Yet Vauxhall Motors had the first machine completed and ready for testing in December 1940, a mere twenty-two weeks after detailed design work began, which was no mean achievement, but at this stage problems arose over the armament. The Department of Tank Design had only started to investigate the arrangement for the 6-pounder turret in November, having failed to anticipate

that the gun itself would be available by this time. Consequently a smaller cast turret for the 2-pounder was supplied. In retrospect it might have been more sensible to fit a larger turret in the first place, capable of mounting the smaller gun but readily adaptable to the bigger weapon as it became available. But there was worse to follow. Even before the first tank was finished it was learned that the supply of 3-inch howitzers for the hull would not be sufficient to complete all of them as planned, so a modification was introduced which allowed a second Besa to be fitted into the hull mounting instead. Tanks so equipped became the Churchill Mark II while the original model carried the designation Mark I – but an even more unusual variant was the Mark I Close Support. In this version the 2-pounder and howitzer changed places: it was not a very demanding project since the mountings were more or less interchangeable, but it does appear to have been a singularly pointless one. By January 1941 two pilot models were on trial, although it would be more accurate to say that they were complete since they spent far more time in the workshops than ever they did out on the test ground. The catalogue of faults seemed endless. Trouble was experienced with the tracks, suspension, gearbox and engine – which was a nest of troubles in itself – while portions of armour plate and special castings were found not to be up to specifications. The standard of work by many of the outside suppliers was so poor that the parent company was obliged to organise special courses of instruction for them, and in some of the worst cases remedial work had to be carried out by Vauxhall themselves. March passed and still no more than two tanks were running (after a fashion) and it was May before the first production machines were available for testing.

Back in February Churchill had insisted that work on the A22 was to be given priority 'in view of its superiority over all other models', but it was a difficult claim to justify at the time. G Vernon Cleare, one of the engineers from Woolwich who was seconded to Vauxhalls, revealed one of the main problems in a paper published in the *Journal of Automotive Engineering* in 1973. He explained that oil and water leaking from the engine and gearbox combined with dust inside the transmission brakedrums to increase friction and create a self-locking effect during steering. A driver, releasing a brake after a sharp turn, would find the tank continuing to swing off course, and would attempt to correct this by applying the opposite brake. This would simply compound the problem and cause enormous stress to build up within the regenerative system, which often resulted in the back plate of the transmission housing being literally blown apart. By June only fourteen production machines had been built, but the delay was aggravated by a change in the gearbox. The original five-speed model was the cause of so much trouble that a four-speed one was substituted. Failures of suspension components were so frequent that in August instructions went out to all crews that the maximum road-speed should not exceed 10 mph, but this was not so much a means of remedying the problem as of staving off disaster for a while. At about the same time the makers, in an unprecedented step, took all ranks concerned into their confidence by inserting a small yellow leaflet into Churchill User Handbooks. It began

POINTS TO WATCH

on early production models of the
infantry tank mark IV

to crews, mechanics and workshop personnel

WE TAKE YOU INTO OUR CONFIDENCE

There are a few features in the design and construction of the Infantry Tank, Mark IV – early models only – which may give rise to troubles not normally expected in service. The object of this booklet is to make those defects known in advance, to all who will handle the vehicle, and to outline the precautionary measures necessary to minimise them.

The defects exist solely because of the inadequate time that has been available for comprehensive testing. They are the "teething troubles" inseparable from a new design. In normal times they would have been eliminated – every one of them – before the vehicle was released for production.

Times, however are not normal. Fighting vehicles are urgently required, and instructions have been received to proceed with the vehicle as it is rather than hold up production.

All those things which we know are not as they should be will be put right . . .

Please do not draw the wrong conclusion from this frank statement of defects. The Mark IV Tank is a good vehicle. The troubles which have emerged from recent tests of the pilot model are not in any way abnormal. The only abnormal factor is that, having found them, we are not in a position to put them right before production begins.

VAUXHALL MOTORS LTD. *May,* 1941

There followed four pages under the separate headings: **Suspension System; Final Drive, Main Brakes and Steering; Brakes; Tracks; Engine; Clutch.** Each was divided into three columns – *early production*, which listed the faults; *precautions necessary*, which told you how to minimise them; and *pending changes in design*, which as candidly as the rest explained what was being done to improve things. It was a remarkable document in many ways and it was right – the Churchill was a good tank as it turned out, but it was a long time proving it. Whether this example of transparent honesty paid dividends is not clear. But there is no doubt that the crews who nursed those early Churchills through their formative months finished up knowing them more intimately than could otherwise have been possible with the most intensive training, and what is more, they soon grew to take a perverse pleasure in operating them.

Construction work on the 6-pounder turret began in August. It was a welded structure of flat plates devised in detail by Babcock and Wilcox, but when it finally appeared it only added to the tale of woe. The first sample failed its initial firing trials and the Bullet Proof Plate Technical Committee was forced to admit that it could not guarantee future supplies of weldable plate which would not flake under fire. As a consequence the War Office authorised another type of cast turret which, in order to keep the weight within acceptable limits, was made of thinner metal. Tanks completed with the welded 6-pounder turret carried the designation Churchill III, and with the cast turret, Churchill IV.

When production was in full swing eleven companies were involved in the actual construction of tanks, drawing

48 *Canadian manned Churchills with a Mark IV leading. Compare its cast turret with the more angular welded type of the Mark III which follows.*

parts from over 600 smaller concerns. At the same time a major rework programme was getting underway. By December 1941 six substantial modifications were being dealt with on service tanks that were steadily being returned to the works. They ranged from alterations to the engines and suspension to the fitting of mudguards over the tracks and a new type of air inlet louvre on the sides. The original pattern drew air in from below, and with it, quantities of dust and leaves. In that same month a pair of reworked tanks arrived for trials in the Middle East, but they had travelled as deck cargo by the long sea route around the Cape and were quite useless. As the first contract neared completion the War Office announced that it had no intention of pursuing the design beyond the present models, pointing out that at one stage nearly half of the tanks issued to units were off the road due to one fault or another. Indeed even after the first reworked tanks were submitted for testing in April 1942 they failed on so many counts that hands were wrung in high places. That this was not the end of the Churchill story we shall see in due course. For now, the fact must be faced that two years after it was first designed the tank was still unbattle-worthy. But it was not the only story of its kind – there was another tank that was even worse.

It was always held to be a truth in engineering circles, notably in the days of steam, that if a machine looked right then invariably it was right. An efficient railway locomotive, for instance, was often also a very good-looking one. Apparently, if the Covenanter is any guide, this maxim does not apply to armoured fighting vehicles. There probably never was a better looking tank; it was compact, sleek and well balanced; there was hardly a vertical surface on it, and the four big roadwheels beneath flared track guards invoked the very essence of speed and aggression. Sadly, it turned out to be a mechanical nightmare on an epic scale.

Yet Covenanter was not another unfortunate product of immoderate haste in design. Work on it began well before the war in answer to a requirement for a new cruiser tank to be both lighter and cheaper than the A16. It was designated A13 Mark III, or Cruiser Mark V, an odd choice since it differed in almost every respect, except the Christie suspension, from earlier models in the A13 series. Design work was placed in the hands of the London, Midland and Scottish Railway Company who set up a drawing office at Euston station to keep in close touch with the Mechanisation Board which supervised the work. The famous locomotive engineer Sir William Stanier, Chief Mechanical Engineer of the LMS, was naturally involved; a genius where railway engines were concerned, he was clearly out of his depth with tanks.

Even from the start things did not look promising. The first prototype featured the full Wilson transmission but in the second and all subsequent production machines, this was changed in favour of a Meadows crash gearbox with Wilson epicyclic steering units bolted to the output

shafts. Then the General Staff demanded an increase in armour standard to 40mm, from the 30mm originally agreed, and the weight went up. A shortage of aluminium for the wheels meant that these had to be produced in steel, which caused a further increase. Covenanter was designed on an all-welded basis, but the L M S expressed doubts about its strength and asked that production models might be riveted; up went the weight again, so that even before the first tank had been built it was calculated that it had reached the maximum weight that the suspension could bear. Thus there was no possibility, even if it turned out to be a successful design, of any retrospective improvements in the way of armour thickness or weapon calibre to keep pace with developments.

The decision to avoid vertical surfaces was not taken, as might be supposed, to enhance the tank's shot-deflecting qualities but simply in order to keep the weight down. However, it resulted in an almost flat hull. The suspension springs were also steeply angled in line with this policy, and for the same reason a new horizontally opposed twelve-cylinder engine, the Meadows DAV of 300hp, was designed specially for it. Even the turret was low – it looked like a squashed version of the type fitted to the A13 Mark II, although in reality it was a completely new design, albeit mounting the usual 2-pounder and coaxial Besa machine-gun. The only other excrescence was the driver's head-cover which was in front of the turret, offset to the right. Since there was nowhere else to mount it the prototype also had a Besa gun in this cab, which the driver was supposed to fire. When it was in place, however, he found it impossible to get into his seat, and it filled the cab with fumes when fired, so it was dropped from production models and a revolver port was provided in its place. The other three crew members occupied the turret which was fitted with a full-width top hatch, called a sunshine roof

49 *When a new railway locomotive was built it was painted matt grey with whitewall tyres for its first photograph. The staff at Crewe continued this tradition when the very first Covenanter was rolled out.*

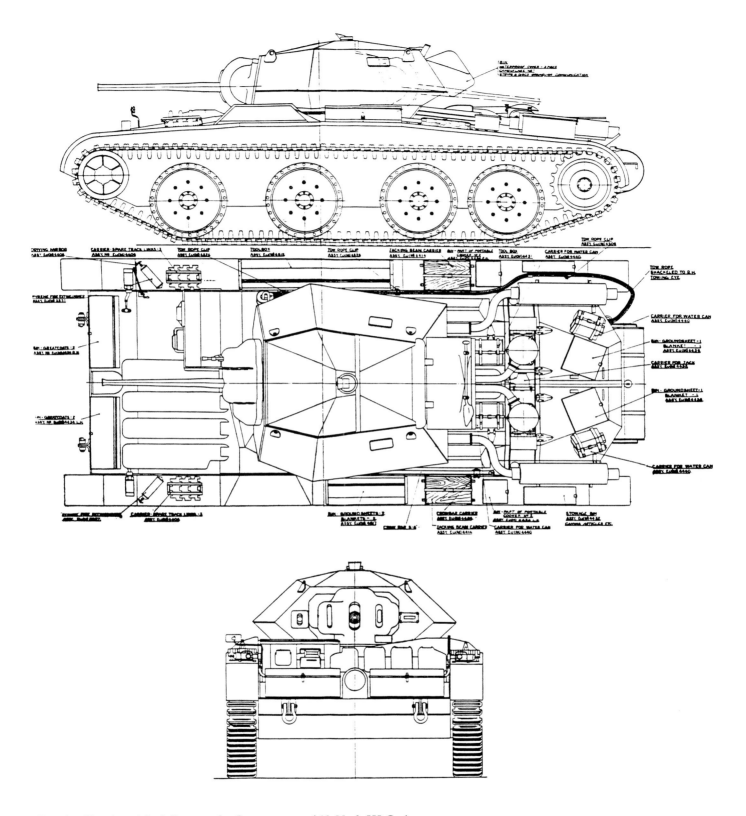

Drawing K: An original diagram of a Covenanter, or A13 Mark III Cruiser.

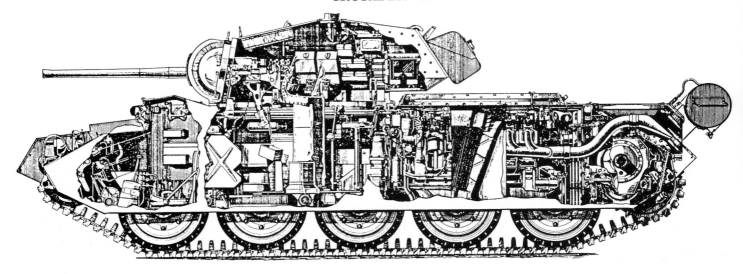

Drawing L: A cutaway diagram of the A15 Crusader II taken from an original vehicle handbook.

because it opened horizontally like the panel in the roof of a car. In the open position it was secured by a catch which was found to be so weak that it came undone when the tank was driving across country, and slid forwards with a force that could decapitate anyone whose head was in the way. Yet the strangest feature of all, and the cause of much subsequent trouble, was the cooling system. A pair of radiators was located at the front, to the left of the driver, and consequently at some distance from the rear-mounted engine they were supposed to cool. The oil cooler too was notably inefficient and attempts to improve one always caused overheating in the other.

When it was running well the tank could travel at a very respectable 30 mph, but the original air-assisted steering system was so unforgiving that it was difficult to hold a straight course, and at high speeds this proved to be very dangerous. Consequently it had to be redesigned, as did the gearbox which, in its original form, churned up oil into a froth. Orders were placed for some 2000 machines with the LMS at their Crewe works, English Electric at Stafford and Leyland Motors at their Kingston plant. Turrets were built by, among others, Allens of Tipton, who had made armoured lorries in the First World War, but supply always lagged behind production of hulls and caused more hold-ups. Thus, although the first contracts were placed in April 1939, deliveries did not begin until after Dunkirk, and Covenanter fell into the same trap as Churchill. The whole programme should have been stopped there and then since it was clear that a great deal of remedial work was necessary to turn it into a battleworthy tank. This would inevitably take so long that the design would be completely out of date by the time it was fit for service.

Covenanters with modified cooling systems were redesignated Mark II, but new production types Marks III and IV, which had these improvements built in, suffered in the same respect, so it is clear that the problem was never really corrected. As if all this were not enough the separation of engine and radiators gave rise to another ridiculous feature. The pipes which carried the coolant from one end of the tank to the other passed along the side of the fighting compartment and were often so hot that they had to be lagged to prevent the crew from burning themselves. Even with the lagging the turret got very warm, something the crew could well do without in the Middle East, so perhaps it is just as well that, apart from a few trial machines, the tanks were never issued for service out there. Although it was desperation which caused them to enter service in the first place the only explanation for their continued manufacture well into 1942 would appear to be lunacy. It seems to indicate something of the stubbornness of British industry at the time, and the lack of firm direction on the part of the Ministry of Supply, which permitted so many useless machines to clog up production lines when far better tanks had been designed and were only waiting for factory space. As a training machine the Covenanter was just about adequate but it was never judged fit for combat service. Yet its very existence helped to put back the production of other cruiser tanks by some two years and, indirectly, led to the loss of many good tank men.

Lord Nuffield was offered the option of joining the Covenanter programme or having his company, Mechanisation and Aero, work on another design. He chose the latter course. This led to the appearance of the unjustly famous Crusader, or Cruiser Mark VI, built to General

50 *The pilot model Crusader shortly after completion. Note that in addition to the forward turret a Besa machine-gun is mounted in the driver's cab.*

Staff specification A15. To make matters more confusing it was the second A15. The first was a heavy cruiser tank proposed in 1937 which would have required a crew of seven. They would be needed to cope with a suggested armament that included a 2-pounder, 3-inch howitzer, two smoke mortars and six machine-guns in a total of three turrets. Fortunately, perhaps, it was rejected before the design had progressed beyond the outline stage.

The Nuffield A15 was a much less ambitious project. It was based on existing A13 technology with the Christie suspension and Liberty engine since the firm had spurned the Meadows flat-twelve unit. Yet it had other features in common with the Covenanter, including the turret and basic hull shape with the raised driver's cab. Again on the prototype an extra Besa was fitted there, and just as quickly removed. But the General Staff insisted, in this case, that the tank must have a forward-firing hull machine-gun with an adequate arc of fire, so a small turret was fitted ahead of the main turret, to the left of the driver's hood. Naturally it was impossible to locate the radiators there as well so they were mounted vertically on either side of the engine, which helped to make the tank that little bit longer than Covenanter. Space was therefore created for an extra wheel-station on each side which gave

the tank a better load-bearing capacity and allowed some scope for later improvement. The Crusader User Handbook made the point that since it was based on A13 fitters should experience no great difficulties in looking after it, although in fact there were significant differences. In place of the clutch and brake steering of earlier models Crusader employed the Covenanter system of Wilson epicyclics in conjunction with the normal gearbox, and it also included pneumatically assisted controls.

Although it had its share of teething troubles there is no doubt that Crusader was a much better tank than Covenanter, if a little bit slower, at 27mph. The first serious problem to be encountered was with the front machine-gun turret. During firing trials at Lulworth, with the tank fully closed down, there was a rapid build-up of gases inside the fighting compartment. The machine-gunner passed out and the rest of the crew suffered severe after-effects. Worst of all the auxiliary turret was so cramped that it proved very difficult to get the unconscious man out, and he was only revived with the aid of oxygen. The Gunnery School recommended that the sub-turret be abandoned, remarking that it took a great deal of courage to shut oneself up in there at all. In the event Mark I Crusaders entered service with it, although it was usually missing from the Mark II because that model was uparmoured from 40mm to 49mm at the front by the addition of an extra sheet of armour which, if cut to full width, covered the aperture. Without this turret, it almost goes without saying, the armament consisted of the 2-pounder and coaxial Besa. It also meant that the crew was reduced from five to four. Production got under way in 1940 with contracts being issued to seven companies in addition to Nuffield, who acted as parents to the group. In due course over 5000 were built although, as events showed, production went on for far too long.

On 26 August 1942 the House of Commons Select Committee on National Expenditure, through their chairman Sir John Wardlaw-Milne MP, presented a report to the Prime Minister entitled 'Weapons for the Army'. They had been asked to prepare it in November 1941 as a result of disquiet expressed both in the House and the press at the state of British tank production. The findings were generally damning and the gist of some parts of the report have already been mentioned in respect of Churchill and Covenanter, but it was also scathing in its conclusions regarding the adoption of the 6-pounder gun, and particularly the efforts made to install it in Crusader.

No matter what else might be said about the British tanks of 1939 and 1940 there was certainly nothing wrong with their guns. Compared with the German equivalent, the 37mm KWK L/46.5, the 2-pounder had twice the effective range and superior penetrating powers. That it was let down at the crucial moment by inferior optics and a shortage of ammunition should not be allowed to detract from its potential. On the other hand its qualities should not have blinded those responsible to the fact that it would soon be necessary to replace it with something bigger and better. Pope had recognised this; writing from France shortly before Dunkirk he urged, among other things, that 'every tank must carry a cannon. The 2-pounder is good enough now, but only just. We *must* mount something better . . .' Yet it is almost incredible to realise that, in 1941, the British Army had six types of cruiser tank and three models of infantry tank in service at the same time, all mounting the same weapon. And this does not include a new light tank and an armoured car. What makes the case even worse is the appreciation that development of these tanks spanned a period of six years. Of course, one of them – the A22 Churchill – was designed with a bigger gun in mind, and two others, Crusader and Valentine, could be adapted to mount it at a pinch, but the others were physically incapable of being upgunned due to the size of their turrets, even if such a weapon had existed. It is not unreasonable to ask why, when the A13 with its Liberty engine and Christie suspension was accepted as a replacement for the A9 and A10, it could not have the facility to take a larger gun built in at the design stage: or why the same thing could not apply to the cruisers Mark V and VI which followed it, in respect of an even bigger weapon. It would be surprising though

if the question drew forth a satisfactory explanation rather than an excuse.

Yet a better gun was already available. The Director of Artillery at Woolwich had initiated the design of a 57mm anti-tank gun, to fire a six-pound shot, on 13 April 1938, and it had been specified then that it should be suitable for mounting on field carriages or in tanks with only minor alterations. There were delays due to shortage of staff and other priorities, and since the Director could get no statement of policy from the General Staff it was early 1940 before the first gun was available for testing, and well into the summer before it had passed these tests at Shoeburyness. The first orders were placed through the Ministry of Supply but production was only allowed to start in a new factory at Radcliffe near Bolton because, as the War Office pointed out, most of the Army's 2-pounder guns had been lost in France, and production of these must not be interfered with. Yet demand increased rapidly until by December 1941 28,000 were on order. The tank version required a different pattern breech-ring compared with the field mounting; it was possible to fit tank guns onto field carriages but not vice versa. However, the Ministry claimed that it was unable to get any clear decision from the War Office on how many of each type might be required. On its own initiative it worked on a ratio of two to one in favour of tanks. Three hundred 6-pounder barrels suitable for fitting into tanks were delivered in December 1941, but since no tanks were ready to receive them they were fitted to field carriages and most sent out to the Middle East.

Meanwhile with two new models of cruiser tank about to enter service a simplified design of coaxial mounting for the 2-pounder and Besa was developed in the summer of 1940. It was built to a 50mm standard against 40mm on the earlier cruisers although, as things turned out, both types of mounting appeared on various types of tank because production overlapped. At the same time another mounting which was anything but simple was being prepared for trials. This appears to have been designed in response to the problem already mentioned of tanks having either a 2-pounder or close-support weapon fitted, when experience in France showed that a dual-purpose gun would be a more sensible arrangement. Since no such gun was available the only alternative was to try and fit both types into one tank, and this had already been achieved, after a fashion, in the Churchill I. The other idea, which was approved by the General Staff in September 1940, was for a triple mounting; a 2-pounder, 3-inch howitzer and 7.92mm Besa machine-gun sharing a common mantlet. A prototype was prepared by Stothert and Pitt of Bath who, no doubt, hoped for substantial orders to follow, which never came. The complications that it promised in terms of ammunition stowage were bad enough, but when one considers the extra strain it would have placed on the gunner and loader the fact of its immediate demise comes as no great surprise.

51 *A close-up of the turret of a Crusader Mark III showing the modifications necessary to fit the bigger 6-pounder gun.*

The failure to match 6-pounder production with that of the Churchill has already been recorded. It remains to examine the situation where cruiser tanks were concerned. Plans were already being prepared for a new tank, the Cruiser Mark VII, to replace Crusader, and this would be designed from the start to accept the new gun. Yet it soon became clear that for a variety of reasons this tank, which was to be named Cromwell, would not be ready by the spring of 1942 as originally forecast, but late summer or autumn at the earliest, so the matter was reconsidered. It will be recalled that at this time the need for cruiser tanks was paramount, so in order to produce an interim design with the 6 pounder, it was decided to try and modify the Crusader.

According to the timetable as reported by the Select Committee, which the Ministry of Supply was forced to agree was substantially correct, the decision to modify the A15 was taken in March 1941, when a mock-up of the new turret was ordered. However even this did not take place without a struggle. A M Durrant, the Director General of Tanks and Transport, claimed that only his department or Vickers were capable of undertaking the project. The latter were already engaged in trying to adapt their

Valentine for the same gun while Durrant's department was fully committed to the design of the 6-pounder turret for the Churchill. In any case, both organisations considered the Crusader scheme impossible and that even a mock-up was a waste of effort, although at one stage they went as far as trying the Churchill turret mock-up on a Crusader hull. It seems, however, that a mock-up was built somehow under the direction of the Ministry of Supply, because General Pope inspected it and said that while it appeared practical it was not very satisfactory. Thus it was not until September 1941 that Nuffields were invited to inspect it, and they discovered so many faults in the design that they undertook to produce a version of their own. This was done and a pilot model built within six weeks, which then went down to Lulworth for gunnery trials. That this was not quite the achievement it appeared to be was made clear by the War Office, who explained that the new turret was nothing more than a modified version of the old 2-pounder type with an enlarged mantlet and redesigned top hatch. The firing trials were completed in November and the first production orders placed on 1 December, with deliveries commencing in the following May. By July 1942 144 had been produced, and about

100 fully equipped Crusader IIIs, as the new model was designated, were available for the battle of Alamein in October.

In their defence the War Office explained that the period of indecision was due to the delay in the Cromwell programme. If things had gone according to plan, they suggested, it would have been wiser to hold out for the new tank rather than disrupt production of the existing one which, after all, would produce a hybrid with many unsatisfactory features. The worst of these, from an operational point of view, was that in order to get the bigger gun in, one turret-crewmember had to be taken out. This brought the total crew of a 6-pounder Crusader down to three because the auxiliary machine-gun turret was not fitted, and the space this released was needed in any case to stow extra ammunition. Thus, in the new turret, the commander also became the gunner while the loader retained his secondary duty as wireless operator, but the extra strain was felt by the entire crew. Even to the uninitiated it is clear that three men cannot undertake the duties of four or five in battle and still expect to maintain the same degree of efficiency – but the difficulties do not end there. When a tank comes out of action the crew has to complete a series of tasks laid down in the Crew Duty Card. These involve such things as servicing the engine and transmission, examining and tensioning the tracks, cleaning the armament, restowing ammunition, keeping wireless watch and cooking a meal. With a bit of luck they might also snatch a few hours' sleep. On top of this there were guard duties and other fatigues of a more general nature, while the commander had to write up reports and attend briefings. When these factors are taken into account it will be appreciated that a three-man tank crew has its work cut out whether in action or not. Yet the two-man turret is not, in fact, the reason why Crusader is included among the unbattleworthy: it was a feature it shared in common with the Valentine, which was otherwise an eminently reliable machine. Crusader's problems were mechanical, but since they did not come to light until it entered service in the desert, they are discussed later.

In July 1941 the newspaper magnate Max Aitken – Lord Beaverbrook – was appointed Minister of Supply. His previous post had been as Minister of Aircraft Production, and it was due in no small part to his energy and drive that the Royal Air Force had been equipped with a modest sufficiency of the best possible fighter aircraft that had enabled them to hold their own during the crucial period of the Battle of Britain. Now, it was fervently hoped, he would do the same thing with tanks.

Within days he had appointed Sir George Usher to the post of Director General of Tank Supply. Following discussions with manufacturers it became clear that the most significant single cause of delay in production was uncertainty. It was generally agreed that changes in priority and a lack of firm policy emanating from the War Office were creating havoc, since the tank builders were never in a position to settle long-term contracts with suppliers of raw materials or component parts. The Ministry therefore sought an agreement with the War Office that would enable them to approach the Treasury for permission to extend the current tank programme until the end of June 1943. By this means, they claimed, orders could be placed for 10,000 tanks in Britain and some 1700 in Canada, as well as whatever might be obtained from the United States under the new Lease-Lend agreement.

The War Office was horrified. In a letter to the Tank Board dated 4 September 1941 the Assistant Chief of the Imperial General Staff, Major General G N Macready, pointed out that if this programme was adhered to at least four types of tank already regarded as obsolescent – Matilda, Valentine, Covenanter and Crusader – would still be in production during the fourth year of the war. It was, he said, like asking men to fight on ponies against an enemy mounted on fullsize horses or, on an individual level, expecting a man with a dagger to fight a duel against a man with a sword. He went on to rehearse recent history, explaining again that the priority had changed in favour of cruiser tanks against infantry tanks. Present requirements aimed at a ratio of 2.5 cruisers to one infantry tank whereas the Ministry's programme, stretching into 1943, would at best produce .9 cruisers to each infantry tank. Furthermore, if the discussion was limited to tanks armed with the 6-pounder gun, by the summer of 1942 there would only be six cruiser tanks and around 1500 Churchills so equipped out of a total of 11,000. By June 1943, Macready said, we should not just be thinking about, but actually building a better machine than any currently specified, mounting a 17-pounder gun, as well as special amphibious and airborne tanks. He ended by calling for an emergency meeting of the Tank Board for Saturday 6 September or Monday 8 September to discuss the matter. The meeting took place on the Tuesday, with the minister present.

Following a reading of Macready's memorandum Beaverbrook was told by the chairman, Geoffrey Burton, that the standing programme could only be changed very slowly. Sir George Usher stated that the Covenanter would cease production towards the end of 1942 and the Matilda by early 1943, when the new Mark VII Cruiser would take their place, but Oliver Lucas, the Director of Tank Design, added that this could only be done by placing the new tank in production before pilot models had been thoroughly tested. Lord Beaverbrook was obliged to announce that the programme for 1942 must stand. After an equally dismal review of the position regarding the 6-pounder gun Lucas informed the War Office representatives Macready and Pope, and the Secretary of State for War, Captain Margesson, that a development of the Mark VII Cruiser with a new engine and transmission was in the design stage. In answer to a request from Margesson for a heavy infantry tank he announced that the Design

Department was investigating three possibilities based on the Churchill, Mark VII Cruiser or the new American T1.

On 9 September 1941 Usher declared that he would have 6000 new tanks built and delivered by the end of June 1942, and following Lord Beaverbrook's visit to Moscow a 'Tanks for Russia' week was declared. It resulted in a brief publicity campaign during which train loads of tanks en route from the factories were seen with 'Tanks for Russia' placards stuck all over them. Since many were Covenanters which nobody, not even the desperate Russians, would be grateful for, it was about as misleading as the inscription 'With care to Petrograd' had been on tanks in the First World War. In the middle of October a luncheon at the Savoy celebrated the end of a 'Speed the Tanks' tour which took Usher to factories all around the country. This had more positive results, since first Lord Nuffield and then the Leyland organisation agreed to put all their available factory space at the disposal of the government for tank production, on condition that they were released from all other commitments, notably the production of wheeled vehicles.

The delay in development of new tanks was blamed on serious hold ups at the Department of Design, and the War Office was offered the pathetic explanation 'quality is desirable, but if quality does not get past the drawing office or the test bench, it will neither do us much good nor the Germans much harm'. On that basis production of the Covenanter might just as well have gone on until Doomsday.

Once Lord Beaverbrook had made his intentions clear and imposed them on both the War Office and manufacturers, it was quite obvious that the British Army could expect no new types of tank until 1943 at the earliest, always excepting those supplied from the United States. Various new designs were on the drawing board, but since these did not begin to appear until production of existing models had ended they need not be discussed here. For the present there was no alternative but to continue training and fighting with whatever was available while industry strove to improve reliability, which was now being seen as the prime requisite in tank design, coming at the head of a list of desirable features which went on to include hitting power and range (of weapon); armour protection; good crew-space, and speed and radius of action, in that order. A review of the tank situation which included that list went on to point out that these tanks were required to operate in conditions as diverse as the hot, abrasive deserts of the Middle East and the frozen wastes of a Russian winter, completely ignoring the fact that German tanks were expected to do exactly the same thing. The same paper went on to summarise the causes which led to improved production. These it saw as the drive of the Minister of Supply and his insistence on a long-term programme; the improved relations that existed between those in charge of production and the contractors, and the detailed planning which ensured a smooth flow of raw materials and parts. At the same time a similar review issued from the War Office contained a statement to the effect that 'The British Army cannot compete, in mere numbers, with the German Army, and operates under the disadvantage of exterior lines'. This last was perfectly true but it was little short of scandalous to suggest that 'mere numbers' was the only other shortcoming. Apart from speed – when they were running well – most of the current range of British tanks were falling behind the German types on all the points listed above as well as others like protected ammunition stowage – and matters such as salvage and repair were not even considered. Even so, mere numbers, notwithstanding the imbalance between infantry and cruiser tanks, was only seen as a short-term problem, pending the delivery of large numbers of American tanks, and the confidence which this instilled should not be ignored. From the date of these documents – December 1941 – reliance upon the United States to make up the shortfall began to dominate the larger picture. There was no longer any doubt that the number of cruiser tanks would be more than sufficient to meet all foreseeable requirements, but there is a distinct, if unstated, impression that the urgency for Britain to develop tanks that were in any way superior to the latest German products had started to fade.

In February 1942 Lord Beaverbrook moved on to the Ministry of Production and Sir Andrew Duncan once again took over the office of Minister of Supply. By early summer the Tank Board was reorganised again under Lord Weir, and Sir William Rootes, among others, became a member, as did W A Robotham of Rolls-Royce, who was already Chief Engineer of Tank Production under Oliver Lucas. Robotham's contribution will be examined later, but for the present it is worth quoting the following statement which was made in a short paper by Major General Crawford, the Deputy Director General of Tank Supply.

The accusation at the present moment [29 June 1942] seems to be that we are producing inferior tanks, both as regards design and fighting ability and that the Ministry could do better. You have seen that four Ministers had [sic] held the responsibility for tank production; one Minister for two terms. The Tank Board has been reconstructed five times, with a continual introduction of fresh ideas. Each has largely endorsed the previous conception.

This country cannot allow a great nation like Germany with its enormous engineering capacity seven years start in the race of tank development and production, and then expect by some miracle unknown to engineering science, to put in the field a force trained and equipped in as many months without paying a heavy price.

Where Crawford got his figure of seven years from is not clear. The tanks Germany was employing in the summer of 1942 dated, in their earliest forms, from 1937, at which time they could only claim to equal their British contemporaries at best. The edge was in reality closer to two years, but perhaps in the rarified atmosphere of war when

52 *Valentines as far as the eye can see. Tanks of 6th Armoured Division at Lakenheath for the King's inspection in September 1942.*

weapons production always accelerates dramatically it seemed more like seven.

Clearly, although it had only run half its course, Lord Beaverbrook's long-term programme was becoming increasingly unacceptable. The source of most agitation was the Middle East. For more than a year now reports had been submitted to the War Office regarding a new model of the Panzer III mounting an effective 5 cm gun, yet the only response appeared to be an endless stream of patently unreliable Crusaders armed with the now discredited 2-pounder. The situation was summed up in a Tank Enquiry conducted by the Secretary of State for Dominion Affairs, Clement Attlee, which was submitted to the War Cabinet at the beginning of June. Although it concentrated on Crusader, he claimed to have unearthed 'a mass of evidence showing that they were merely symptomatic of a host of similar troubles'. The suggestions of complacency and inertia in all quarters in both this and General Crawford's paper could be blamed on a number of factors: the curse of direction by committee, departmental loyalties, and the cohesive team spirit, all of which tend to excuse or deflect criticism rather than react to it. But

things were coming to a head. Sir George Usher was one who did not mind rocking the boat. He was actually responding to the previously mentioned report by the Select Committee on National Expenditure which appeared in August 1942 when he said that in his view, once a tank had passed beyond the prototype stage all responsibility for its future development should come under the direct control of the individual or organisation responsible for producing the finished article.

Comparing the entire tank production set-up to a commercial company he pointed out that the present system was equivalent to investing different executives with the responsibility for design and supply under the remote control of the company chairman. Thus the managing director, whose job it was to ensure that the customer got what he wanted, had no control whatever over his design staff who could make changes in the product without reference to anyone but the chairman. Given his business background and experience in both Britain and America it was a fair analogy, but expecting the War Office and Civil Service to follow his thinking was, perhaps, a case of the most naive optimism.

In the meantime the Tank Board had been revised yet again with the appointment, at the end of August, of Commander E R Micklem as chairman. Micklem, a retired naval officer, was until that time with Vickers, who agreed to release him. Unlike his predecessors in the chair Micklem would have executive control over research and development, design, testing and supply, for which purpose an Armoured Fighting Vehicle Division was set up within the Ministry. Micklem was, therefore, chairman of that too. This came into effect early in September. Micklem's first step was to issue a memorandum on a proposed reorganisation which Sir George Usher thought should be discussed before it was released. He felt that he had the support of Sir William Rootes since the latter came from a similar industrial background but, when the crunch came, he found that he was virtually alone. To Usher, Micklem's proposals amounted to no significant change at all, and after a few days of intensive meetings and correspondence he resigned. Three senior members of his department went with him.

In September 1942, while this drama was being enacted behind the scenes, a display of armoured might was being arranged for the King. The entire 6th Armoured Division was assembling at Lakenheath in Suffolk to parade before His Majesty and then drive past in review order. The armoured element of the Division at this time consisted of one armoured car regiment, the 1st Derbyshire Yeomanry and 20th Armoured Brigade, comprising 1st Royal Gloucestershire Hussars; 1st Northamptonshire Yeomanry; 2nd Northamptonshire Yeomanry; and the 26th Armoured Brigade, comprising 16/5th Lancers; 17/21st Lancers and 2nd Lothian and Border Horse. In all, there were fifty-eight armoured cars and 340 tanks, along with 4020 other vehicles belonging to the two infantry motor battalions, three artillery regiments, one infantry battalion and two field squadrons of Royal Engineers, manned by some 15,000 troops. It was an awe-inspiring sight, never before seen in one place at the same time. Its very bulk came as a profound shock to those who previously had never seen them as anything more than columns of words and figures on an establishment table. Now it could clearly be seen that the Division was top heavy in armour, and the result was that in a short time the tables were rewritten to show only one armoured brigade per division, the other being replaced by a motorised infantry brigade to produce a more balanced force.

5 Tracks in the sand

53 *Matildas of 7th RTR refuelling prior to the attack on Bardia. The tank on the right is having its track repaired.*

If the situation in Britain was looking bad after Dunkirk it was no better in Egypt, nor had it ever been since war was declared. The relative importance accorded to each theatre changed almost annually in the years immediately before the war as Mussolini and Hitler alternately rattled their swords. Towards the end of 1937 it was the Italian dictator's turn. Just before Christmas, at a meeting in the War Office, the Chief of the Imperial General Staff reviewed the situation and posed the question 'where was the Army most liable to fight?' He concluded that 'the continental commitment was cut out, the Middle East was undoubtedly the danger spot'. What was to be done about it? The meeting had to decide what types of tank would be required, and agreed in the first place that it would be best, for reasons of supply and maintenance, to choose as few different types as possible. Yet account had to be taken of both tactical and financial matters, so in the end it appeared that compromise was the only answer: 'we must get what we can, rather than what we like'.

The most serious threat was seen as an Italian advance out of Libya with the British Army on the defensive, but a second stage was envisaged as a combined air and ground counterattack with the RAF acting as spearhead, backed up by mechanised ground forces. The CIGS felt that too much attention should not be paid to tank versus tank conflict, nor the use of tanks against well-prepared anti-tank defences. Rather, he visualised a situation where close cooperation existed between the two forces so that aircraft would make opportunities for armour to exploit. Although it is not spelt out in the reports it is clear that his thinking was based on the use of light tanks which,

after all, were all that was available. The most telling phrases are these: 'if the war were to spread to Europe, as may well occur, medium tanks would be required. He did not visualise this occurring for some considerable time.'

Although it would be in the North African desert, in Libya and Egypt, that the war in the Middle East would be decided, it was by no means the only danger zone from the British point of view. A substantial force was still required to keep the peace in Palestine, which had only been achieved by firm intervention in 1936. The Italians were also present in strength in Abyssinia where they threatened both Kenya and the Sudan. Conversely the French presence in Syria to the north east and Morocco and Algeria in the west provided some comfort.

The Munich crisis in September 1938 diverted attention once again to Europe although the continental commitment was still seen largely as a French responsibility. From the British point of view Egypt and the Suez Canal remained top priority. Since no tanks could be spared the War Office did the next best thing and sent out a man who was regarded as one of the country's leading exponents of armoured warfare, Major General P C S Hobart. He was a man who could inspire immense loyalty or intense dislike, but never indifference. Unfortunately the favourable response usually came from subordinates while antipathy often lodged in the bosom of a superior. Starting in 1934 he had raised the 1st Tank Brigade to a peak of efficiency before being translated to the War Office, where he proceeded to make uncompromising waves. The task that faced him now was daunting. There were five armoured regiments in Egypt at this time, the 11th Hussars who had recently moved down from Palestine with their armoured cars, the 1st and 6th Battalions RTC and the recently mechanised 7th and 8th Hussars. These, along with units of the Royal Horse Artillery and 1st Battalion the King's Royal Rifle Corps, formed the Mobile Division (Egypt) which spent most of its time alternating between Cairo and the western railhead at Mersah Matruh as the Italian threat blew hot and cold. Although the division included two armoured brigades it was not up to strength, since each brigade only comprised two regiments and these were so poorly equipped that in 1935 it was referred to scathingly as the Mobile Farce. The 11th Hussars, despite the fact that it was included as part of the Light Armoured Brigade, was in effect the divisional armoured car regiment, for which role it was equipped with those same Morris light-armoured cars that its sister regiment, 12th Lancers, took to France, and modified Rolls-Royces that dated back to the early 1920s. Otherwise this brigade comprised 7th Hussars in light tanks and 8th Hussars who managed for the timebeing in Ford trucks mounting light machine-guns. The Heavy Armoured Brigade was no better off. 1st RTC had a mixture of two and three-man light tanks while the 6th had the same, stiffened, if that is the right word, by some venerable Vickers Mediums that were now so worn out they rarely ventured far from Cairo. The other element of the division formed the pivot group; the RHA fielding 25-pounders and 37mm anti-tank guns while the KRRC formed the motor battalion.

When Hobart arrived, at the end of September 1938, the Mobile Division less the virtually immobile 6th RTC was at Mersah Matruh, but in October the tension eased and he brought it back to Cairo to begin intensive training. In March 1939 they went out into the desert again for a few weeks' field training, and by the time they returned to Cairo Hobart had succeeded in achieving a level of efficiency and morale which more than compensated for the dismal state of their equipment. When war was declared against Germany all units were brought to a state of immediate readiness and a month later, in October, ten A9 Cruiser tanks arrived to replace the Mediums of what was now, officially, 6th Royal Tank Regiment. Yet all remained quiet. While German troops moved in to occupy Norway and the Low Countries Italy held its peace, but once it became clear that France was on its last legs Mussolini made his move. At a stroke the situation changed dramatically, for the fall of France removed not only that country but all its overseas possessions from the equation, and British forces in the Middle East were decisively outnumbered.

In the meantime the Mobile Division was retitled 7th Armoured Division and its brigades renumbered and restructured. The 4th Armoured Brigade now comprised 7th Hussars and 6th RTR, while 8th Hussars and 1st RTR formed 7th Armoured Brigade. Sufficient cruiser tanks had now arrived to permit each regiment to field

one squadron at least, but only the 11th Hussars, with their armoured cars, were ready to take any offensive action. Even before some of the Italian frontier garrisons knew they were at war the armoured cars struck, capturing the forts at Sidi Omar and later Capuzzo with relative ease. It was a fine example of audacity combined with mobility since the cars were very lightly armed. In order to bring them into line with the Morris type the Rolls-Royces had been modified in Cairo. The original turrets had been replaced by flat sided, open-top contraptions mounting a Boys rifle, Bren gun and smoke discharger.

The tanks came forward again in July. The distance from the railhead and base camp at Mersah Matruh to the Italian wire along the Cyrenacian border was 120 miles and all of this had to be covered by the tanks on their tracks since no transporters were available. Reserve crews were employed to drive them but nothing could be done to ease the wear and tear on the tanks themselves. Although the soft sand made steering easier it permeated everywhere and the abrasive effect was serious. Despite the fact that the British had considerable experience of operating tanks in desert conditions, and that the area had been seen as an important operational theatre since the mid 1930s, very little effort appears to have been made, in terms of design, to prepare the tanks specially for the region. As an example, it was discovered that the air filters on early cruisers, A9s and A10s, were inadequate and a new two-stage pattern had to be developed. Likewise, when the first A13s arrived it was discovered that their Liberty engines were particularly vulnerable on account of the exposed valve-gear along the top of each bank of cylinders. The strain on the armour was not helped by General Wavell's choice of tactics. Rather than assaulting and occupying the Italian forts he employed raiding techniques, much as T E Lawrence had done in 1917, to tie down the maximum number of enemy troops while he destroyed their supply columns. For their part the Italians were handicapped mainly by the excessive caution of their senior commanders and by the types of armoured fighting vehicle available to them. The majority were little better than armoured carriers – although referred to by the British as light tanks – which had developed from, and still bore a striking resemblance to, the Carden-Loyd type of 1928. With a pair of forward-firing machine-guns they were of even less use in combat than the British light tanks. Their principal medium tank was the model M11/39 which carried its main armament – an effective 37mm gun – in the hull front, with a machine gun only in the turret. Satisfactory as it may have been in the direct assault role it was at a severe disadvantage when the need arose to fight other tanks in the open, as the British were to discover two years later with the Grant. British tactics usually involved sweeping down on a convoy unannounced, firing at the halt for greater accuracy and then moving on to the next target. By the time the driver of an M11 had swung his machine round to bring his main gun to bear his target

54 *The 11th Hussars scouting towards Bardia. The car is basically a 1924 pattern Rolls-Royce, modified by the Nairn Transport Company in Cairo to accept an open-top turret. The radiator has also been fitted with a condenser, in the shape of a small can.*

was gone. A new medium tank, the M13/40, was just entering service and this carried an excellent 47mm gun in the turret. Used aggressively it was at least the equal of contemporary British cruisers and with its V8 diesel engine probably a good deal more reliable, but with a few notable exceptions the Italians erred on the side of caution to a degree that nearly proved fatal.

After a month of this armoured guerilla warfare the British tanks were beginning to fail mechanically. At any one time 7th Armoured Division could only count on two thirds of its meagre strength and by August the bulk had been withdrawn to Mersah Matruh to refit, in case the anticipated Italian invasion caught all of them in the care of the Light Aid Detachments, Royal Army Ordnance Corps (RAOC). With the pressure thus lifted the Italians finally made a move in force, although it lacked the elan

of a *blitzkrieg*. It took them four days to cover half the distance (60 miles) from the frontier to Mersah Matruh in the face of only the most modest resistance, but it seems to have exhausted their initiative. At Sidi Barrani they settled down and proceeded to establish another series of fortified posts in the coastal region which were so spaced out as to be incapable of mutual support. Indeed the gaps between them were so wide that armoured cars of 11th Hussars regularly passed through on their way to reconnoitre areas behind the Italian positions.

Italy's entry into the war seemed to have closed the Mediterranean to British shipping so in future convoys bound for Egypt made their way into the South Atlantic, around the Cape and up the Red Sea to unload their vital cargoes. Thus, although Britain's presence in the region was ostensibly as a safeguard for the Suez Canal, its use, for all practical purposes, was virtually denied to them anyway. The longer sea route not only delayed the arrival of reinforcements, it had a detrimental effect on tanks and gave a certain element on board more time to pilfer valuable tools and other useful items from this vulnerable source. It was by this route that three more armoured regiments arrived from Britain late in September 1940. They had sailed four weeks earlier, on 21 August, and considering that this was less than two months after the BEF had been unceremoniously evicted from Europe, it implies a major effort to supply sufficient tanks. All the same one regiment, 3rd Hussars, was only equipped with light tanks and they went to join 7th Armoured Brigade. Second RTR fielded cruisers, mostly A13s with a few A9s and A10s; they joined 4th Armoured Brigade. Seventh RTR operated A12 Matildas, the first to arrive in a theatre of war where they were destined to gain such a fine reputation, and after training they joined 4th Indian Division for an undisclosed purpose. On the instruction of Major General O'Moore Creagh, commanding 7th Armoured Division (Hobart having been effectively sacked late in 1939), one squadron each from 2nd RTR and 3rd Hussars traded places so that the latter could at least field some 2-pounder armed tanks.

Now that he had more strength to his elbow, and satisfied that the Italians were not about to launch a decisive blow against the Nile Delta, Wavell decided once again to take the initiative. The result was staggering, but it has been recounted in detail so many times that only the barest outline is necessary here. The object of the operation was to take advantage of the moral superiority which, it was believed, the British had gained over the Italians during the preceding months, to hit the enemy hard and discourage them further while the situation in the Sudan was cleared up. Five days were all that was to be allowed and the plan involved a direct assault on the Italian positions by the Matildas of 7th RTR and 4th Indian Division; the event for which they had been training together. While this was taking place the more lightly armoured tanks of 7th Armoured Division would sweep around the entire position to prevent any reinforcements getting through. Taking advantage of the widely spaced enemy strongpoints the main assault force would first approach Sidi Barrani from the south and then swing quickly round to launch its attack from the west.

Following a two-day approach march, during which time the Italians seem to have done nothing in the way of ground or aerial reconnaissance the attack went in early on 9 December. Coming from the least expected direction and spearheaded by tanks that were all but immune to enemy anti-tank weapons, it was a complete success. All the outlying camps were taken on the first day while Sidi Barrani itself was taken on the following day with assistance from 4th Armoured Brigade. Soon the Italian defence collapsed completely and thousands of men were only too willing to surrender and even organise their own transport into captivity. The rest made off in the opposite direction, abandoning some camps that had not yet even been threatened, and by 12 December they were back behind the wire of their own frontier. But it did not end there. Although he removed 4th Indian Division for his proposed campaign in the Sudan, Wavell allowed 7th Armoured Division to proceed into Libya to follow up its success. Attempts were made to cut off large sections of the retreating force, although they failed to stop them from falling back on and settling firmly into Bardia. The final stage of this first period of action was an assault on 16 December by 7th Hussars and 2nd RTR against the frontier fort of Sidi Omar, which was achieved in the remarkably short time of ten minutes by an attack, as usual, from the west, or 'Italian' side.

Both men and machines were now thoroughly worn out and a lull ensued while crews rested and tanks were recovered and repaired. Nothing more could be done until a new infantry division, 6th Australian, arrived to replace the Indians. More had been achieved than even the most optimistic could have hoped, and even better was to come, but in taking stock at this intermediate stage it can be seen that a great deal had been due to 7th RTR and its Matildas. Although they lacked the speed and range of the cruisers they more than made up for it with invincibility. At the same time much credit was still due to the absent Hobart. When 6th RTR was attacking Sidi Barrani it ran into a fierce sandstorm and only managed to keep together and maintain direction by the quality of their wireless discipline, the very cornerstone of Hobart's training. The entire operation had been a fine example of the correct use of armour and, it should be noted, without any really effective help from the RAF. The Italians had lost the initiative at the outset and their high command had let them down badly, but their artillerymen deserve credit. Most stuck to their guns until they were overrun or shot down. On the other hand the infantry were realists, almost to a man. As soon as they found themselves involved at close quarters with tanks that shrugged off their fire they acted with impeccable discretion.

On 6 January, following a carefully rehearsed plan, Bardia was attacked and fell three days later. Once again it was the depleted 7th RTR that bore the brunt of the fighting, but it is noteworthy that the Australian infantry brigade which began its attack from the south without the aid of tanks made the least progress until the six Matildas still fit for action were sent across to assist. Immediately the fall of Bardia was assured 7th Armoured Division made another westward push to envelop Tobruk. Effective tank strengths were now down to a very dangerous level – and it should not be forgotten that a considerable proportion still consisted of the relatively useless light tanks. Indeed things had reached such a state that 6th RTR handed over all its surviving machines to 1st and 2nd, and returned to Egypt. After a supreme effort 7th RTR, which all this time had been serving as Corps troops and not part of the division, could only muster sixteen operational Matildas for this next stage. Considering what Tobruk became as a symbol of resistance over the next few months, it is amazing to record that it fell in two days to a combined Anglo-Australian attack. Its garrison at the time amounted to over 25,000 men, more than 200 guns and eighty-seven tanks.

The continuing success of this improvised campaign created a dilemma for Wavell, who was being urged by London to find troops for other operations. Clearly it would be foolish to stop now but, at the same time he was disinclined to provide reinforcements – so if anything more could be done it was up to 7th Armoured Division to do it. For the time being 7th RTR had shot its bolt and was withdrawn, but the next stage was all about mobility over vast distances, and that was more than could be expected of a few worn-out Matildas with exhausted crews. They had already journeyed over 200 miles of desert on their tracks and it was time to go back to Egypt and refit. The next major objective was the port of Benghazi on the western shore of the great northern bulge of Cyrenacia. Rather than follow the Italians round that long coastline 4th Armoured Brigade, on the day that Tobruk fell, made another dash for the inland settlement of El Mechili which contained a strong Italian garrison. Forty eight hours was allowed for the 100 mile trip but it was completed in seventeen. The attack began on the morning of 24 January, but the light tanks of 7th Hussars met their match in the Italian mediums which drove them off. Soon a squadron of cruisers from 2nd RTR intervened, and the boot was on the other foot. However, El Mechili was a difficult place to encircle and it proved impossible to contain the enemy force, which soon made off in the direction of Benghazi.

There followed a few days of indecision before permission was received to push on for Benghazi, but even as this was being planned news came in of a general Italian retreat from the entire promontory. It was clear that if they could get far enough around the coast to occupy Agheila the Italians would achieve a decided strategic advantage, and the only way to prevent this was by an interception along the coast road, somewhere between these two places. It was a daunting prospect for it involved a journey of some 150 miles, at the best possible speed, across rugged terrain. If they got there these battle-weary tanks would then be more than 450 miles from their starting point at Mersah Matruh, and the state of most of them is not difficult to imagine. Fourth Armoured Brigade, escorted by the armoured cars of 11th Hussars, set off on the morning of 4 February with 1st RTR – the only remaining operational regiment of 7th Armoured Brigade – in their wake. They soon ran into trouble. After two hours' driving they ran into an area of hard, jagged rocks which could only be negotiated with the greatest care at a snail's pace. Now they learned that the Italian retreat had begun in earnest so the tanks altered course

to strike the coast road further south, around Beda Fomm. In the pious hope that wheeled vehicles would make better time the 11th Hussars and a mixed column of artillery and motorised infantry were ordered to make a dash for the road, but due to bad going they never got far ahead of the tanks. Even so, by mid-afternoon on the 5th they succeeded in blocking the highway south of Beda Fomm where they found the head of the Italian column just coming on. In response to urgent signals some of the fast A13 cruisers of 2nd RTR raced over the final thirty miles, coming into action at once.

What followed was a disaster of the first magnitude for the Italians. For the next two days, in a series of running battles, a skeleton force of light and cruiser tanks all but wiped out a vastly superior Italian force of all arms. It was achieved by a combination of audacity and superior tactics since the British tanks took every possible advantage of ground, sprinting from one hull-down position to another, halting to fire and then sweeping round again to attack from another direction. Clinging to the road, hampered by confused infantry and abandoned lorries, the Italian tanks failed to combine in large enough numbers to achieve anything worthwhile and they were destroyed piecemeal. It was a notable victory by any standards and crowned a remarkable campaign that began as a five-day holding action. Much of the credit for this masterpiece of improvisation was due to the men on the spot, but as they were quick to acknowledge it could never have been achieved without the thorough grounding that 7th Armoured Division, in particular, had received from General Hobart. By this time that officer was about to start a new phase in his career, having been presented with the task of raising and training a new armoured division, the 11th. Before then, and almost since his return from Egypt, he had been forced into premature retirement and wasted a vital year as a member of the Home Guard.

An official training pamphlet, 'Lessons of the Cyrenaica Campaign' which was issued in 1942 likened the success of 13 Corps – as the Western Desert Force had latterly become – to the defeat of the Spanish Armada in 1588; the Battle of Britain might have been chosen as a more up to date parallel. It went on to say 'The honour of this campaign must go to the Armoured Fighting Vehicles, which throughout the period were the spearhead of all operations whether mobile or deliberate. The country favoured armoured operations and the very most was made of that advantage'. In view of such euphoria it would possibly be a bit unkind to examine how they behaved in too much detail, but in the light of events in France it makes for interesting comparisons.

Of all types of armoured vehicle employed the most heavily worked must have been the armoured cars. Eleventh Hussars had been in action almost continuously from the day that war was declared and they probably covered the greatest mileage of all. Without a doubt the Rolls-Royces were the most venerable, having been built in 1924. Most of them had been in the Middle East since 1927. On those grounds alone their performance must be considered as remarkable and this can only be attributed to their inherent quality and the dedication and experience of their crews. Although they lacked four-wheel drive and even a half-respectable armament they appear never to have let the side down on any important occasion. It should be noted in passing that a few more Rolls-Royces, some of even greater age, were operated by No 2 Armoured Car Company, Royal Air Force in the later stages of the campaign and these retained the original Vickers gun-turrets. The RAF was in the process of fitting these armoured hulls on to new Fordson truck chassis in order to give them a new lease of life and the conversion also involved adding a Boys rifle and stripped Lewis guns to the turret with an extra, armoured wireless operators compartment in the back. The Morris light armoured cars, of which thirty served with 11th Hussars, also did well. Indeed when fitted with large-section sand-tyres they were often found to be better on soft going than the Rolls-Royces, but then they were a good ten years younger. On the other hand their springs did not stand up so well to the punishing terrain and they were rather underpowered. It would be the last campaign for both types. One report, published at the end of the war, suggests that a few Guy armoured cars (the so-called wheeled tanks) were also operating in the Western Desert at this time although no contemporary evidence can be found. It seems that if anything their behaviour was even worse than those in service at home for the report says that almost all of them were abandoned at a very early stage, which may account for the silence.

The light tanks performed very well but they had been in the desert for some time and their crews were used to them. They certainly stood the pace of operations but, as in France, their inability to deal with other tanks was a handicap. This was made even worse, according to one report, by the fact that no .5 inch ammunition was available for the heavy machine-gun at all. The .303 was perfectly serviceable although the need to keep the cooling jacket filled with water added even more to the general shortage of that precious commodity.

This was even more true of the Cruiser Mark I (the A9) which mounted three Vickers guns, but in every other respect it was more than a match for its Italian rivals, and the same was true of A10. Both tanks were praised for their reliable engines and simple transmission while tracks and suspension stood up well to the desert conditions. It is worth noting that where failure and defeat gave rise to criticism, success and victory generated praise – but they were the same tanks. Mainstay of the cruiser tank force was the A13 with its Christie suspension. Photographic evidence indicates that the Mark IV type, with slightly thicker armour, was used exclusively, and it was much praised for its speed, especially in the last dash to Beda Fomm. On the debit side the tracks were criticised, as

they had been in France, for being too narrow and prone to break. Clutch trouble was also fairly common and, as already explained, the Liberty engine was badly affected by gritty dust on the exposed valves.

Without a doubt it was the Matilda that stole the show. Its thick armour allowed it to roam the battlefield at will, immune from anything the Italians could fire at it, but it was not entirely free from faults. Clutch trouble was experienced, mainly on account of the twin-engine layout. Unless both engine clutches were finely balanced one or the other would inevitably take most of the strain during starting and consequently burned out. On the other hand performance was improved in later models; from the Mark III onwards a pair of Leyland diesel engines, delivering 190hp, replaced the AECs which only gave 174hp. The problems associated with the Rackham steering clutches in France were not so evident in the desert, since for one thing it was often possible to move for long distances in a fairly straight line. For another, the soft sand offered far less resistance to slewing than heavier European soils, so the strain was reduced. Yet the potential problem was appreciated and when the tanks were required to negotiate the sharp hairpin bends of the road which climbed the escarpment near Halfaya, the Matildas were roped up to Scammell artillery tractors which literally pulled them round the corners. The smooth tracks that had given so much trouble in France were not a problem in Libya – indeed, this pattern was preferred to the heavily spudded type.

The Matilda was certainly slow and for that reason not suited to far-ranging pursuit operations, which they had never been designed for. The fact that they achieved what they did was due in no small part to the wisdom of Lieutenant Colonel R M Jerram, commanding 7th RTR. Jerram insisted that during any approach march his tanks should proceed at about half their maximum speed to avoid unnecessary wear and tear. He could, he agreed, move a lot faster if it was accepted that many of them would suffer breakdowns en route, but if he was allowed

55 *In order to reduce wear on their steering clutches during the winding climb over Halfaya Pass these Matildas were hitched up to Scammell gun-tractors which pulled them round the sharp corners.*

a bit more time he could guarantee to get his entire force to the appointed place fit for action. His advice was heeded and the regiment succeeded beyond all hopes.

In general, then, the tanks that had performed so dismally in France were a great success in the desert theatre. Obviously this was due largely to the way they were handled and the fact that the machines they were opposed to were decidedly inferior. Despite their reliable engines the Italian tanks were easy prey for the 2-pounder gun and their armour in particular was of poor quality. The absence of a high-explosive capability was not commented on at this stage, probably because the Italians made such bad use of their anti-tank guns that there was no need for it. Gun for gun the 2-pounder had the edge on the 47mm, and due to the brittle plate, Italian tanks were often penetrated before they could get within effective range. It was a situation that would change dramatically in a few months. Operationally too the British tanks were handled with far greater understanding. Officers and men of the Royal Armoured Corps serving in the desert at this time deserve comparison with the best of the Panzer crews that had subdued the Allied forces in France with such apparent ease a few months earlier. The Italian 10th Army employed traditional tactics in which the tank was seen as a weapon subservient to the infantry, and this was no way to behave in such open country.

The fact that they had not been mentioned in the forgoing account of events in Libya should not be taken to imply that vehicles of the Bren Carrier family were not present. On the contrary, large numbers were employed by infantry and machine-gun battalions in addition to 6th Australian Light Cavalry which operated them in lieu of tanks. Indeed, the first tanks that this famous regiment used in action, during the attack on Tobruk, were some captured Italian mediums, M11s and M13s, which they marked conspicuously with large white kangaroos to avoid mistakes. In retrospect perhaps this was an unnecessary measure because the Australian manned tanks were handled in such an aggressive way compared with the style of their former owners that there was little doubt who was in them. During the British swoop on Beda Fomm the mechanised units of 6th Australian Division followed the retreating Italians around the coast, through Derna to Benghazi, which they captured.

Returning to the carriers, both Bren and Scout types were used in the desert although in terms of numbers they were soon over-shadowed by the Universal which was taking part in its first campaign. Generally all versions

56 *A Universal Carrier leads a Scout Carrier past the ruin of Fort Capuzzo. Both vehicles carry Boys rifles in their front compartments.*

performed well. Mobility remained good either on sand or rocky ground and the main faults were a high incidence of track breakage and a tendency for the rubber tyres to become detached from roadwheels in very hot weather. The Universal also began to show signs of suffering from a weight problem. The extra armour added about half a ton to the weight compared with a Bren Carrier, while the extra available space created an unavoidable tendency to overload. This had a detrimental effect on performance and led to an increase in the mileage done in lower gears, which resulted in premature transmission failure.

Rarely in the history of warfare can the potential fruits of complete victory have been thrown away with such a lack of prescience as they were after Beda Fomm, although inevitably there were excuses. The desperate shortage of operational AFVs, general exhaustion among the fighting troops and politically inspired pressures on the Commander in Chief all contributed. But total victory was within Wavell's grasp and he failed to hold it. Eleventh Hussars led British forces ninety miles beyond Beda Fomm to El Agheila, and from there found the road to Tripoli open, and ripe for exploitation. But they did not have sufficient equipment to push on and, in any case, four days later they were officially ordered to stay where they were.

At the end of February 1941, with all quiet on the Western Desert front, 7th Armoured Division was withdrawn from El Agheila and replaced by 2nd Armoured Division which had arrived in Egypt piecemeal late in 1940. There was such a switching round of regiments that the change was hardly obvious. First King's Dragoon Guards, recently converted to an armoured-car regiment, took over from 11th Hussars and inherited most of their surviving Morris and Rolls-Royce machines to supplement its newly acquired Marmon-Herringtons. 5th RTR – of 3rd Armoured Brigade – came up in support but in their haste to get on station managed to wear out a large proportion of their cruiser tanks (mostly A13s) in the process. With them came 3rd Hussars and the men of 6th RTR. Third Hussars had two squadrons of badly worn light-tanks so they equipped their third with M13/40 mediums captured at Beda Fomm. Sixth RTR had no tanks at all so they were fitted out entirely with Italian machines which were swiftly modified to accept the British No 11 wireless set. Lacking air support, since all but one fighter squadron had been withdrawn for other operations, 3rd Armoured Brigade and 7th Australian Division trained, patrolled and awaited development. They would not have to wait long.

General Wavell's responsibilities in the Sudan have already been alluded to. The number of British tanks involved in the campaign was tiny, but effective nonetheless. Five A10 cruisers and three light tanks detached from B Squadron, 6th RTR took part in the attack on the Italian fort at Gallabat in October 1940 which proved successful despite the fact that the cruisers were all immobilised by broken tracks on the stony ground. Then, in January 1941, B Squadron, 4th RTR, with sixteen Matildas and one Light Mark VI, took part in the attack on Eritrea where they encountered a well-led Italian army and some of the least promising tank country in the world. Following some hard fighting and even harder travelling the campaign was successfully completed in just two months.

The real fly in the ointment, as far as Britain's chances of success in the Mediterranean were concerned, was the attempt to penetrate the Balkans from Greece. It was a pet project of Churchill's, imposed upon a reluctant Greek government that was doing perfectly well against the Italians on its own. The tank element of this British force was 1st Armoured Brigade Group, consisting of 4th Hussars in light tanks and 3rd RTR which had been hastily equipped with the weary A10s of 5th RTR. It was a hard-fought campaign which can only be summarised here. Arriving early in March 1941 1st Armoured Brigade had only a month to settle in before the Germans invaded and by the end of April it was out again, leaving all its armour behind. Within another month the island of Crete had fallen to German airborne troops, who also collected six Matildas belonging to 7th RTR and sixteen light tanks of 3rd Hussars. In both cases, however, substantial numbers of RAC personnel were safely evacuated to Egypt. Other vulnerable locations in the Mediterranean received small allocations of tanks which could hardly have been expected to repulse any serious attempt at invasion, no matter what they might have done for local morale. A Special Tank Squadron of Valentines operated in Gibraltar, which was unlikely tank country to say the least, while No 1 Independent Troop RAC was sent to Malta. It was equipped with a few Light Mark VIC and Matilda tanks which were noteworthy more for their 'crazy paving' style of camouflage than for anything else they did. Cyprus was held in larger numbers, if not greater fighting strength, by 7th Australian Cavalry who fielded one squadron of light tanks and two others in trucks.

Further east things were more serious. Unrest in Iraq was held in check by the RAF with their vintage Fordson/Rolls-Royce armoured cars and some Italian Lancias which they probably picked up after Beda Fomm. Iran was occupied by an Anglo/Soviet force that included the Indian Army's 13th Lancers who were still equipped with old Crossley/Chevrolets of North West Frontier days. The biggest problem of all was Syria, where it became necessary to subdue Vichy French forces. The British fielded one squadron of the Royals, recently converted to armoured cars, while 6th and 9th Australian Cavalry operated in light tanks and carriers. They were no match for the French medium tanks and, as a consequence, took heavy losses although by the end of the campaign, in July 1941, both Australian regiments could boast a few Renault R35s on their strength.

Drawn inexorably into the Mediterranean theatre, first by the Italian failure to subdue Greece and then by the

57   A Royal Air Force armoured car—a Rolls-Royce hull on a Fordson chassis—near Baghdad. In addition to the Vickers machine-gun there is a Boys rifle to the left and a Lewis gun on top of the turret. At the rear one can just make out the armoured wireless compartment with its top hatch open.

British threat to drive them out of North Africa, Hitler decided to reinforce them with a German corps under the command of General Erwin Rommel. He could not have made a better choice. A relatively recent convert to the armour creed, Rommel assiduously studied the pre-war British theorists and drew all the right conclusions from the latest British actions. With only one regiment – the 5th – of his 15th Panzer Division yet landed at Tripoli, Rommel, as Wavell had done with the Italians, made a tentative move forward on 31 March 1941. This probing attack started the alarm bells ringing in 2nd Armoured Division and after further contact General Neame, acting on a sanction in Wavell's orders, began to withdraw from a reasonably defensible position into the open desert, aiming to fall back on Benghazi. Second Armoured Division, as already explained, was short both in equipment and training. Rommel brought more than just men and tanks with him to North Africa, he also carried a formidable reputation. This wasn't personal – at this stage he was virtually unknown to the British Army – but a general one attributed to the German Army, and the Panzers in

particular. Since they had failed to capture a single German tank in France the British relied on rumour, and when this reached the army in Egypt it spoke of 'huge streamlined monsters' and 'enormous eight wheeled land-ships' whereas in fact the embryo Afrika Korps only had 106 tanks, about one third of which were little better armed than the British light tanks. Even the vaunted eight wheelers mounted nothing more terrifying than machine guns. The true German strength lay in that audacious use of mobility which the British had employed to overawe the Italians only nine months previously. Indeed the German strength was enhanced by a mass of dummy tanks, hastily put together in Tripoli and mounted on Volkswagen chassis.

Within two weeks Rommel had chased the British and Australian troops clear across the Egyptian border, with the exception of Tobruk which they managed to hold. To the scattered British units as they made their way back towards safety the Germans appeared to be everywhere. With the capture of General Neame and General O'Connor effective overall command was lost, and much of 2nd Armoured Division was surrounded and captured at El Mechili. That Tobruk was held owed a great deal to the odd assortment of British tanks now residing there. These included two squadrons of 1st RTR equipped with light tanks and cruisers, and a mixed squadron of 3rd Hussars and 5th RTR in similar machines. They were joined in April by some Matildas of 7th RTR which arrived by sea on 19 April, and between them they held off the attacks by Rommel's rapidly growing force which now included three more Italian divisions, Ariete, Brescia and Trento. Holding a thirty-mile perimeter against such attacks was a formidable task but it was achieved by the intelligent use of artillery and minefields, stubborn resistance from infantry outposts and well-directed counterattacks by the tanks, which were kept back to intervene in force wherever a breakthrough had been detected. Rommel gave up the attempt at the end of April.

Believing, perhaps, that the Germans had shot their bolt for the present, and anxious not to give them any chance to settle in, Wavell decided on an operation to dislodge them from the closer frontier positions. Although considerable reinforcements were on the way from Britain he found that he could muster sufficient tanks to complete two regiments from salvaged and repaired stocks in Egypt. As a further measure, and an indication of just how desperate things were, even the few surviving medium tanks were brought back to Mersah Matruh and dug in, until only their turrets showed above the sand. Thus, in addition to the ubiquitous 11th Hussars who were already on the frontier, 2nd RTR came forward with a collection of venerable cruisers, while 4th RTR turned up two squadrons strong – B Squadron still being engaged in Eritrea – with twenty-six Matildas. It was the latter's task to force the enemy out of Halfaya Pass, while the more mobile cruiser regiment swung round to the south with the object of cutting the road between Capuzzo and Tobruk. The Matildas did well at first, taking the Pass and Sollum, but there were too few of them; even tanks put temporarily out of action by minor breakdown or damage depleted stocks sufficiently to inhibit further action. As enemy resistance increased they were gradually withdrawn. Second RTR fared even worse. In fact it never got beyond Capuzzo due to a combination of vigorous German reaction and increasing instances of mechanical breakdown in tanks which were already on their last legs.

The reinforcements referred to in the previous paragraph were so desperately needed that on the Prime Minister's special instruction, in the face of much Admiralty opposition, a special convoy codenamed 'Tiger' was despatched to Alexandria via the shorter route through the Mediterranean. It comprised five fast, modern motor ships heavily escorted by the Royal Navy, since in addition to the Italian fleet the German Luftwaffe was now present in strength on Sicily. Although the MV *Empire Song* struck a mine and blew up south of Malta – taking fifty-seven tanks to the bottom with her – the remaining ships delivered 238 to Egypt: 135 Matildas, eight-two cruisers and twenty-one lights which might just as well have been left behind. The first Crusaders had arrived in the desert. It needs to be stressed that at this stage, in almost every quarter, it was firmly believed that the Crusader was an excellent tank. Admittedly the Gunnery School had condemned the auxiliary machine-gun turret as unfit for human habitation in European conditions, let alone the desert, but in all other respects it was being hailed as a vast improvement over anything that had gone before, and especially when compared with its contemporary, the Covenanter. The faults that would reveal themselves in the next few months could hardly be anticipated and there is little doubt that the men of 6th RTR who were to receive them looked forward eagerly to the experience. The convoy arrived on 12 May, and with the Crusaders spoken for the Matildas went to 4th and 7th RTR, the former now made up to full establishment with the Eritrean adventure behind them. Where the light tanks went nobody said and it probably did not matter. Although Wavell was keen to mount a new operation, with the intention of driving the Axis forces back to Tripoli, as soon as possible it was clear that some time was needed to prepare the tanks for desert conditions, and especially in the case of 6th RTR to familiarise the men with their new charges.

At the same time a scheme was devised to disguise tanks and it was first applied to the newly arrived Matildas.

It was the exact opposite of Rommel's scheme to make Volkswagens look like tanks; a method of making tanks look like lorries. A suitably finished canvas on a frame structure was fitted over the entire hull. Known by the codename Sunshield, one of the claimants for its invention was the stage magician Jasper Maskelyene, then serving as a Major with the Royal Engineers, who ran a curious but highly inventive unit that specialised in deceptive measures. The camouflaged tanks also dragged a few track links behind them to wipe out the distinctive trails they made in the sand. Dummy tanks were employed too so that in theory tanks would appear to be where they were not, and not appear to be where they really were. To what extent it fooled the Germans is not known, but Maskelyene claimed that it made a difference to enemy dispositions at Alamein.

Wavell hoped to use his new-found tank strength to eliminate the enemy in North Africa, but the delay in preparing them for action meant that this ambition had to be modified into a scheme to drive them west of Tobruk and relieve the besieged garrison. Scheduled to begin around the middle of June 1941, under the codename Battleaxe, the scheme was based on the assumption that, at worst, there was parity in the number of tanks available to both sides. In fact, as later research has shown, the British had an advantage of around two to one in gun-armed tanks if the Germans and Italians employed every machine available to them. One interesting feature was that the four tank regiments which formed 7th Armoured Division at this time all belonged to the Royal Tank Regiment. Fourth Armoured Brigade consisted of 4th and 7th RTR, both equipped with Matildas, while 2nd and 6th RTR were with 7th Armoured Brigade. The former had two mixed squadrons of A9 and A10 cruisers while the third fielded A13s. Sixth, as already mentioned, was fully equipped with Crusaders which were about to see action for the first time. Each brigade was therefore short of armour to the tune of one regiment apiece. The cavalry element was represented, almost inevitably, by the experienced and highly regarded 11th Hussars with their armoured cars.

Battleaxe is a difficult and disappointing operation to describe, even in outline. As Wellington might have said the British came on in the usual way and got repulsed in the usual way, but this is an oversimplification. Fourth Armoured Brigade, with their infantry tanks, supported 4th Indian Division in a direct assault on Halfaya and Capuzzo, while the cruisers of 7th Armoured Brigade swung around the southern flank to tackle the Hafid Ridge, west of Capuzzo, with a view to driving on to Tobruk. Working under the command of unsympathetic senior officers the Matilda regiments were broken up into squadron strength forces and thrown against positions which included a few well-sited 88 mm anti-aircraft guns which Rommel employed in the anti-tank role. They were emplaced behind stone breastworks which left only the menacing, horizontal muzzles protruding over the lip. They could pick off a Matilda at ranges of well over half a mile whereas the tanks had to close to about half that distance to have any effect at all. Even then the chances of scoring a direct hit with solid shot from a moving tank on such a tiny target were slim indeed, and the need for a gun capable of delivering a decent high-explosive round was felt once again. Artillery support was the only satisfactory alternative, but due to an unfortunate set of circumstances C Squadron, 4th RTR lost theirs before the attack began and went in alone against the 88s which effectively wiped them out. Seventh RTR did better, since it functioned as a complete regiment, and after taking and holding Capuzzo it was joined on the second day, 16 June, by the surviving tanks of its sister regiment.

While the Matildas were slogging it out with the anti-tank guns 7th Armoured Brigade was making its wide, flanking sweep to the south. Second RTR led the way with the two squadrons of A9s and A10s making the initial assault upon the frontier positions. Once these were broken the A13s of B Squadron made a dash for the Hafid Ridge where they became mixed up among the enemy

58   An A13 cruiser tank pretending to be a rather large lorry with the aid of a Sunshield disguise. Notice how the road wheels have been painted to highlight the effect.

guns. Relying on their speed they did considerable damage but then withdrew, leaving the position in German hands. Later in the day two squadrons of Crusaders came up, but by this time Rommel had reinforced the area with more tanks, and following a long-range fire fight both were forced to pull back having lost about half their number, many with mechanical trouble. Plans for the second day had to be modified in the face of increasing German pressure as the first elements of 5th Light Division began to arrive from the Tobruk perimeter, and 8th Panzer Regiment, of 15th Panzer Division, moved down from the direction of Bardia. In response to this threat, and taking into account the heavy tank losses on the first day, the surviving tanks of all four British regiments were ordered to cover a withdrawal, which they did with a good deal of skill and courage. On the third day the disengagement was successfully completed before the Germans were able to cut them off.

It is impossible to make an orderly retreat from a messy battle and then try to claim that you have won it, but there were some redeeming features. In most of the actual tank fighting the British exhibited a good deal more dash and daring than their opponents, and command, at both regimental and squadron level, was of a very high order, especially in view of the fact that a shortage of wireless sets meant that they were only available on the scale of one per troop. The fault lay with senior commanders who caused the tanks to be split up during the attack stage. This led to units remaining separated when the counter-attacks came in, which was clearly to the Germans' advantage. Initial tank losses were probably about equal on both sides but in the long run it was the British who lost most because they were left behind on a battlefield that the Germans still occupied. The Germans, on the other hand, were able to recover most of their casualties for repair. The biggest disappointment of all was the performance of the Crusaders. Even when they were working well it was impossible to take advantage of their otherwise impressive speed since the rocky ground prevented them from using it. When they were not running well it was a positive liability.

Battleaxe also marked the end of Wavell's career in the desert and much was expected of his replacement, General Auchinleck. That this theatre was seen as far more significant from London than from Berlin is clear from the respective scale of reinforcements that were now delivered to both sides. Rommel received a relatively small infusion of gun tanks, although nothing like enough to warrant the formation of any new Panzer regiments, and some more 88mm guns. He did, however, acquire a new type of long-barrelled 50mm anti-tank gun in some numbers, which was significant not just for its greater penetrative powers but for the mobile way in which it was employed. Likewise, among his stock of Panzer IIIs a far higher proportion was equipped with a 50mm weapon, albeit shorter and less powerful than the latest anti-tank version. The

British, on the other hand, received a substantial transfusion to both their land and air forces. Of the Royal Armoured Corps, by November 1941, the following regiments and tanks were operating in the Western Desert:

1st Army Tank Brigade, comprising
8th RTR in Valentines
42nd RTR in Matildas
44th RTR in Matildas

22nd Armoured Brigade, comprising
2nd Royal Gloucestershire Yeomanry
3rd County of London Yeomanry
4th County of London Yeomanry
all in Crusaders

4th Armoured Brigade, comprising
3rd RTR
5th RTR
8th Hussars,
all in American M3 (Stuart) Light Tanks

7th Armoured Brigade, comprising
2nd RTR
6th RTR
7th Hussars,
mainly in Crusaders but still with some
A10 and A13 cruisers

32nd Army Tank Brigade (in Tobruk), comprising
1st RTR in cruisers
4th RTR in Matildas
D Squadron 7th RTR in Matildas.

The balance of 7th RTR was employed on deception and tank delivery duties. In addition most regiments still fielded a few Mark VI Light tanks. It should hardly be necessary to emphasise yet again that apart from the Stuarts which their mildly superior 37mm guns, all tanks listed still mounted the inevitable 2-pounders. Nor should one forget the armoured cars – Marmon-Herringtons were pretty well universal by now – serving with the Royals, King's Dragoon Guards and 11th Hussars. Despite this massive preponderance in armour Auchinleck steadfastly refused the Prime Minister's demands that he should commit any of it to action until he was good and ready. His plan was to use it in one massive attack which would, once and for all, drive the Axis armies clear out of the desert arena and back across the Mediterranean, which he planned to achieve in the first place by the total destruction of their armour. The operation, christened 'Crusader', was to commence on 18 November 1941; five days before Rommel intended to make his own assault on Tobruk.

All told the British fielded over 750 tanks against about 400 of both German and Italian origin. And it was the tanks that would decide the issue; how they were handled and how many survived when the crunch came, no matter how well the other arms fought. Leadership, skill and courage notwithstanding it was numbers that would ultimately prove the key factor. Leaving 4th Indian Division to contain the Halfaya, Sidi Omar, Capuzzo triangle the main force would sweep round, well to the south, and then strike north west in the general direction of Tobruk. Here, it was hoped, they would find and destroy the bulk of the Axis armour. Yet despite the change in command and the infusion of new blood it was very much the mixture as before. Furthest out in the desert were 22nd and 7th Armoured Brigades with 4th Armoured Brigade to their north, all operating relatively fast cruiser-tanks. Further north still, and closest to the Sidi Omar position, was 1st Army Tank Brigade with its infantry tanks, whose task it was to back up those forces facing the frontier positions. Thirty-second Army Tank Brigade was under orders to break out from Tobruk as soon as the opportunity presented itself.

To anyone who imagines that the entire Western Desert is a sea of rolling sand dunes, baking beneath an eternal sun, it comes as quite a shock to read of torrential rain and tanks getting bogged down in the mud. Yet these conditions affected both sides during the opening days of Crusader. The weather also interfered with the operations of Axis aircraft which were unable to fly out of flooded airfields and spot the British advance. All the same, German dispositions were such that they were quickly able to recover from the initial surprise and start hitting back. The battle that followed was one of the most intense and finely balanced of any during the early part of the war. Regiments, brigades and divisions of tanks swept in and out of action, wheeling over hundreds of square miles with fortunes changing hourly. The drive for Tobruk ran into trouble some thirty miles south east of the port, on a German airfield at Sidi Rezegh, and it was possession of the high ground near here that would decide the battle, all other factors being equal. The first week, until 24 November, was characterised by a great deal of confusion and surprise. Large bodies of tanks would suddenly appear from entirely unexpected directions to catch their opponents off guard, and soon the area would be littered with burning tanks.

Overall it is clear that Rommel retained the best grip on the situation and kept the initiative while the British, despite air superiority, were often caught on the hop. British armoured units became dispersed and often nearly destroyed in detail before the situation could be retrieved, and any attempt to concentrate was frustrated by another German attack. With no clear front line to aim for, a roving armoured column was just as likely to encounter an enemy headquarters group or supply convoy as it was other tanks. The objective of destroying the Axis armour by overwhelming it proved impossible in such fluid conditions and, indeed, there were times when the opposite result appeared to be the likely outcome. If traits can be detected they are almost caricatures. The British all too often allowed themselves to be drawn onto emplaced anti-tank guns or hull – down tanks which they always attacked with the utmost courage, to their own cost. The Germans kept themselves under close control, fought tenaciously

when the situation demanded, preferably from a position of strength, but refused to be drawn into needless sacrifice. The Italians were even more careful but now they were decidedly under German control, and deep in the shadow of the Afrika Korps they made poor allies. In the middle of a hot-blooded fight they could be formidable but a long approach-march seemed to sap their resolve and reduce their speed to a crawl. The German General Crüwell's oft repeated cry 'Where's Gambara?' (General Gambara commanding XXth Italian Corps) became the standing German joke of the battle.

Both sides evinced a tendency to overestimate enemy casualties, especially in numbers of tanks destroyed. This prompted the Tobruk Garrison to make a premature breakout and nearly brought about its destruction. But on the 24th it caused Rommel to launch an attack to the east which he expected would round up and destroy the remaining British forces in Libya. He was defeated more by overstretched supply lines and a consequent shortage of fuel than by any specific British actions, although the depleted regiments of the Royal Armoured Corps continued to harrass him at every turn. The result was inevitable. From 26 November onwards, although it was not realised at the time, Rommel began a withdrawal that would carry him back to the old position west of Beda Fomm. It was in no sense a rout – on the 27th there was another major action around Sidi Rezegh which lasted for six days – but following a final unsuccessful attempt to re-establish contact with the frontier positions around Bardia he began, slowly, to pull back. His tanks situation was getting desperate, while the British regiments were building up again from a healthy reserve of 300 machines that were coming up from Egypt, and with many others recovered from the slowly clearing battlefield. Yet the British remained cautious, especially as their supply lines lengthened. Rommel was not going with his tail between his legs; on 26 December at Agedabia his Panzers surrounded and all but annihilated 22nd Armoured Brigade, after which Auchinleck decided to push no further. The Germans were given the chance they needed to recover their strength and it only remained for the British to recover Bardia. It fell to a night attack by 8th and 44th RTR on 1 January 1942.

It is now time, once again, to review the performance of those Allied tanks which had recently joined the ranks of the Eighth Army. The new star was undoubtedly the Valentine, if only on account of its inherent reliability. The majority of these tanks used in the desert at this time were Marks II and IV. The former carried a diesel version of the AEC engine fitted to the Mark I, while the latter used a GMC diesel engine instead. Otherwise they were almost identical to the Mark I, although improved tracks were being supplied and, as it became available, the No 19 wireless set was steadily replacing the old No 11 model. Although, at this stage, the Valentine was employed exclusively in its designed role as an infantry tank, in reality it

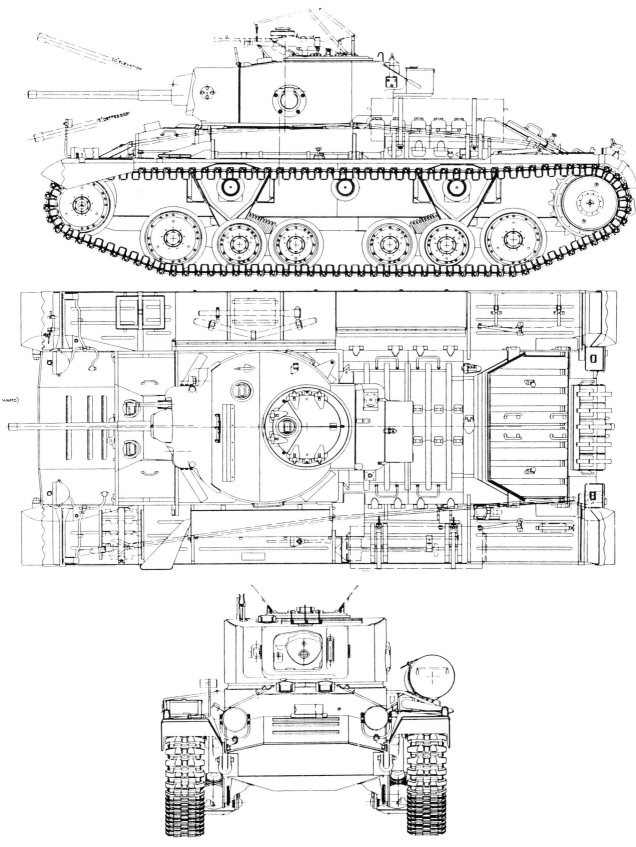

Drawing M: *A later version of the Valentine with the three-man turret. Compare the mantlet and hatch arrangement with the Mark I.*

59 *Valentines on a desert hillside. The tank on the left has its turret pistol port open and, to protect the glass, a pair of steel helmets over the headlights.*

fell between two stools. In terms of armour protection it was no match for the Matilda, but by 1941 standards it was a bit too slow for a cruiser tank. Like the Matilda it suffered from the apparent disadvantage of not having a hull machine-gun, although this rarely seems to have attracted any adverse comment in respect of either tank. One feature that did was the odd hatch arrangements for the driver's cab. Apart from a tiny hinged block in front of his face a Valentine's driver only had a large access or escape hatch on each side – the panel above his head was a fixed part of the hull. It was therefore impossible for him to drive with his head outside, which most drivers preferred to do when they were not in action. The two-man turret was always unpopular, and work was proceeding in Britain to design a bigger one to take three men. When it appeared, tanks so equipped were designated Mark III (with the AEC diesel) and Mark V (when fitted with the GMC). Also, it should be noted, the low silhouette of the tank was an advantage; it was possible to secrete it in a fairly shallow fold in the ground.

The American M3 Light Tank – officially the General Stuart I to the British – was the first transatlantic type to see active service with the British Army and, as such, might well have been the target for a lot of biased criticism. In the event it became a firm favourite – a Honey – for two reasons; reliability and simplicity. In a region where approach marches could be measured in tens of miles (over 100 was by no means uncommon) it always stood the pace and remained mobile and trustworthy in action. Armour protection was on a par with A10 and the later A13s while the riveted construction of the early models was not singled out as cause for complaint since it was just as common with British machines. The Stuart was powered by a seven-cylinder Continental engine designed for use in aircraft. It was an air-cooled radial which appears to have performed very well under armour

in all climates, and it gave the tank a top speed that compared favourably with the Crusader. Unlike the British, American designers tended to favour a dispersed drive train to give better weight distribution. British cruiser and infantry tanks of the period all had their engines, gearboxes and final drive behind the turret, driving the rear track sprockets. Mechanically this is always reckoned to be the most efficient system since the tracks are not subjected to so much tension. The Americans placed the engine at the back but then led the drive shaft through the fighting compartment to a gearbox and final drive at the front. Not only was this less efficient for the reason stated above, it also took up a lot of space and caused their tanks to have a higher silhouette, which was not always welcome in the desert.

Apart from those tanks built by Vickers-Armstrong the majority of British tanks also featured quite complex and sophisticated steering systems which not only absorbed less engine power but also provided the facility of a neutral turn whereby the tank could spin round on its own axis in a tight space. In the United States a form of controlled differential was preferred, which was a lot simpler to manufacture and maintain but did not allow for such tight turns. Indeed, the quoted minimum turning-circle for a Stuart was forty feet, although in the desert this hardly mattered very much. The Americans have always had a penchant for machine-guns and the M3 sported no less than five of them. In addition to the normal coaxial fitting, and another in the hull front to the right of the driver (like most American tanks the Stuart was lefthand drive), two more were installed, one at each side, in the hull where it widened over the track guards. These mountings were rigid and the guns would be fired by remote control, on the same bearing as the tank, but with far more effect than accuracy. Before long British crews lost interest in them and had the openings plated over, providing a bit more precious stowage-space inside. The fifth gun was fitted to a pintle on the commander's cupola so that he might not feel left out. Popular as it was the Honey still had some vices and the worst of these were in the turret. Both the elevating and traversing handwheels were badly located, according to British practice, and all the tanks that arrived in Egypt had first to be modified before being issued for service. Even then it proved to be an extremely awkward arrangement which seems to have led to a reluctance to traverse the turret during an action. Stuart II was the British designation for a version of this tank equipped with a Guiberson nine-cylinder radial diesel-engine.

Following the successful conclusion of the operation that bore its name, and with six months' desert service behind it, the Crusader was starting to show up as a very unreliable machine. That the major faults were with minor components did not lessen their seriousness nor the time needed to put them right, and it did not help that the worst of them were directly concerned with the cooling arrangements. Two particular ones were identified; the

60 *A brand new M3 Stuart light tank, freshly painted and stowed by the book, of 8th Hussars takes part in an exercise in Libya. The date is August 1941 but the tank will not look as neat as this for long.*

radiator fan drive and the water pump. A Crusader had a pair of 19-inch fans located between the front of the engine and the fighting compartment, driven by a loop of exposed chain from a sprocket on the crankshaft. The wear on both items was found to be excessive while the task of replacing them involved a major exercise in stripping out adjacent fittings. The seals on the water pump failed regularly as did the white metal bearings. The main cause of both was gritty sand carried round by the coolant but there is some evidence to indicate that it was aggravated by the practice of driving the tanks a short distance – on

the dockside in Britain – with their radiators drained. Local modifications were evolved but there appears to have been no display of urgency to get to the root of the problems and solve them once and for all. When, ultimately, this was done it was too late, for by then the tanks had such an evil reputation that troops could hardly be persuaded to operate them. Oil leaks were another problem. They could be found everywhere, but the worst, and most consistent, occurred in the pipes feeding the engine sump. They could only be cured by lifting the engine out of the tank. Most of these faults could be traced to poor workmanship which, when it led to unnecessary losses in action, caused a howl of protest. Perhaps, in the desert, it was easy to forget what conditions were like in Britain. Tanks, and indeed all military products, were designed, assembled, delivered and loaded aboard ship under the most trying conditions. Bombing was only the most dangerous of a whole host of problems that beset every citizen during the daily round, and if workmanship suffered as a result it was hardly surprising. On the other hand, as far as tanks were concerned, the quest for reliability was not helped by a policy that expected manufacturers to undertake the final inspection of their own products.

One other problem experienced with Crusader in action was a matter of faulty design. It involved the engine air-cleaners, which for reasons of space were located outside the hull, on the rear track-guards. Finding the ideal location for air cleaners is never easy, but of all places external mountings are probably the worst. They are liable to pick up far more dirt than would otherwise be the case, and therefore clog up more quickly, and they were not only vulnerable to enemy fire but also to blasts from the tank's own gun if it happened to be firing to the rear. A visit by a team of engineers from Nuffield to the Western Desert resulted in improved standards of production and the development of a heavy-duty fan drive-sprocket. The first consignment of these was rushed out to Egypt aboard the cruiser *HMS Newcastle* in April 1942.

The fighting that took place in the desert always tends to fascinate. It came as close as anything could at that time to a clean war, with more emphasis on respect than atrocity and only the minimal amount of suffering on the part of the civilian population. We will return to it shortly, having looked at another aspect of the tank story.

6 Missionaries in Washington

61 Grampus *at Aberdeen Proving Ground in September 1940. Although the burly sergeant looks impassive the Americans were not very impressed with the British tank.*

Before embarking upon this aspect of the tank story it is probably a good idea to get the subject of overseas aid into perspective. According to statistics quoted in the Official History of the Second World War,★ throughout the period of hostilities Britain supplied herself and the Commonwealth and Empire countries with 69.5 per cent of the munitions that were required from her own resources. The remaining 30.5 per cent came in part from those countries but mainly from the United States of America.

America was the obvious country to turn to if one required anything with which to fight a war. Its industrial potential was massive and free from any risk of enemy interference while the attitude at government and presidential level was favourable to the Allies. Against this,

★M M Postan, *British War Production*, HMSO, 1952.

when the war broke out, was that industry was geared almost entirely to the manufacture of commercial items, so any changeover to military production was bound to be slow, and anything purchased would still have to be transported long distances by sea at the mercy of U-Boats and enemy surface-raiders. Furthermore, a strict Neutrality Act was in force. Many Americans blamed their country's involvement in the First World War on a pro-Allied bias in the interpretation of neutrality, so the Act forbade the sale, to belligerents, of munitions of any kind. Indirect warlike stores such as machine tools and trucks could be purchased, and the French government soon placed large orders for the latter, but even then the Act made it illegal to carry them in neutral, especially American ships, and no loans or credit facilities were available; everything had to be paid for in dollars or gold.

Canada, of course, was involved in the war from the start so no such inhibitions applied, although its industrial capacity came nowhere near to matching that of the USA. It was here that a British Purchasing Board was established early in the war which, among other things, investigated the possibility of producing tanks in that country.

From this sprang a British Purchasing Commission, under the Rt Hon A B Purvis, which opened an office in New York to coordinate matters from there, mostly the supply of machine tools at this stage. By November 1939 the situation in America went through a subtle change with the repeal of the Neutrality Act. It was argued in Congress that in practice the Act ran counter to its intentions, because America was prevented from assisting those nations it regarded as representing the free world unless it, too, went to war – when it would naturally cease to be neutral. In theory at least this repeal permitted American companies to trade with any of the belligerents, but as far as the Germans were concerned there was a catch. America still insisted that such material must be paid for and shipped in vessels which flew the flag of the country that bought them; what President Roosevelt described as a cash and carry system. This effectively debarred the Germans from such trade while, on the surface at least, the Royal Navy still ruled the waves. Orders were then placed for transmission and suspension units for Valentine tanks. They would be delivered either to Britain, where the tank was already in production, or to Canada where it was planned to start building them soon.

Meanwhile across the Atlantic events unfolded towards the disaster of June 1940. In Britain, among those affected in a peripheral way was Michael Dewar, the head of British Timken Ltd, who had served in the Ministry of Munitions in the First World War. Dewar's country house in Hertfordshire became, for a time, the headquarters of the Heavy Armoured Brigade, and from some of its officers he learned of the appalling state of tank production. Following a meeting with Winston Churchill, still First Lord of the Admiralty at this point, he was advised to make representations directly to the War Office since Churchill was far too busy to involve himself at that time. These approaches proved fruitless but they did bring Dewar into contact with Harry Ainsworth, the General Manager of Hotchkiss et Cie in France, who was trying to interest the British in his model H39 tank. As already explained this effort came to nothing, and under the circumstances it is just as well, as in any case the Hotchkiss was really an unsuitable model by British standards. Ainsworth, obviously, had a vested interest in the deal but in backing it Dewar reveals his own lack of knowledge about the virtues of AFVs. Above all else he was impressed by the French use of large castings to form the hull, as compared with British riveting techniques, but he failed to appreciate its shortcomings. This emphasises once again the extent to which unenlightened amateurs felt that they could advise on tank matters.

When France capitulated and Churchill became Prime Minister he put Dewar in touch with Herbert Morrison, the Minister of Supply. Dewar claims that it was largely due to his advice that Sir Peter Bennett was sacked from the Directorate of Tanks and Transport and replaced by Geoffrey Burton. In addition to the work it was doing in Britain the Ministry of Supply now had plans to place large orders for tanks in the United States. They had two models in mind, the A12 Matilda and A15 Crusader, but their procurement would require supervision, so Morrison asked Dewar to go to America and undertake this work. Dewar agreed and took with him a small team of experts, although they did not all travel together. This British Tank Mission included Mr L E Carr, a tank design expert from the Mechanisation Board, and Brigadier D H Pratt who had commanded 1st Army Tank Brigade (4th and 7th RTR) in France during the Arras fighting. In addition to the fact that even in the civilian clothes which strict observance of neutrality obliged him to wear Douglas Pratt looked every inch the archetypal British officer, he embodied all the experience of recent tank fighting that the British possessed.

The first members of the Tank Mission arrived in New York late in July 1940 to make contact with Purvis. Although nominally subordinate to the British Purchasing Commission, they functioned at an entirely different level. The BPC dealt with wider issues at the highest level while Dewar's team were nuts and bolts men, working directly with the manufacturers. It was not a good time to arrive in the United States. The fall of France induced a profound shock and it was widely believed, even by the British Ambassador Lord Lothian, that it would be Britain's turn next. Many American companies had undertaken to supply large numbers of trucks to the French and it now appeared that these would not be paid for. Despite Britain's demonstration of goodwill in taking over all of these contracts American industry would, in future, insist on substantial down-payments before accepting any more orders. There was another slightly ominous change that Dewar noticed. The Americans were now showing a marked resistance to the idea of building British-designed tanks at all. This was not a case of national pride; before France capitulated an Allied team which included Louis Renault had been laying plans to build the Char B1-BIS over there and Harry Ainsworth, who also appeared on the scene, claimed that he had a contract with the Blaw-Knox tractor company to build Hotchkiss tanks. The trouble was that now, no matter what the American public might think, the Roosevelt administration knew that it was only a matter of time before they would be directly involved in the war and when that happened the country would need all its available capacity to build tanks for its own army. Thus it made good sense to insist that the British accept American designs so that production, once established, could be used to supply the US Army at the appropriate time.

62 *In October 1940 the wooden mock-up of the Medium Tank M3 was photographed at Aberdeen, where it was also inspected by Douglas Pratt.*

Within forty-eight hours of his arrival in New York Dewar realised that it was not the ideal base of operations for the Tank Mission. The people they needed to deal with were in Washington and the capital was also within easy reach of the main tank evaluation establishment at Aberdeen Proving Ground. All the same, besides being hot and humid in summer, Washington was extremely crowded and office space was at a premium. But Dewar had strong business connections in the USA. In addition to the obvious link with the parent Timken Company, he was associated with the Cincinnati Milling Machine Co, whose president put his suite of rooms in the Carlton Hotel at the mission's disposal. Here, in lounge, bedrooms and even the bathroom, they set up office and home.

Under pressure from the Ministry of Supply in London Dewar did his best to obtain contracts for Matilda and Crusader but he soon came to realise that it was a forlorn hope. Yet it seemed impossible to convince London of this, and in late August the British Tank Mission was embarrassed to discover that another mission, under Major-General Pakenham-Walsh, had arrived with the same object in view. For a while this bemused the Americans who were unsure with whom to deal but the new team was soon as convinced as Dewar's that British requirements would never be met, and when this was backed up by Purvis from New York the authorities in

Britain were forced to recognise the facts. Even so the British attitude is understandable. Although they had adopted the Christie suspension system, which the US Ordnance Board would not touch, they had little faith in America's ability to design a battleworthy tank and good reason to believe that their own recent experience of tank fighting gave them considerable authority in the matter. Certainly the tanks then being produced in the United States did not appear calculated to inspire confidence, but these were desperate times and one gets the impression that this was something the Tank Board and the Ministry of Supply could not bring themselves to comprehend.

According to their own system of nomenclature the first item of any store to enter production for military purposes in America was designated M1, whether it was a heavy tank or a bayonet; the second was M2, and so on. Additional letters and digits signified improvements to the basic type. Thus in 1940 the production Medium tank was the M2A1 and the light tank the M2A4. Both of them had the merit of innate mechanical reliability although their potential as fighting machines was questionable. Dewar's first attempt to interest the British Army in the medium tank failed but a wooden mock-up of a new model, the M3, was soon available at Aberdeen Proving Ground for inspection. Douglas Pratt, now promoted to Major General, went to have a look at it and returned dismayed. It was, he said 'as high as the Tower of Babel' and when London heard about it they were even less impressed. The high superstructure was due not only to the engine and transmission layout which was the same as the M3 light tank already described, but also to the mounting of the main armament in the front of the hull, offset to the right. The gun itself, however, was a vast improvement on anything the British had yet managed to fit into a tank: it was a 75mm dual-purpose weapon which could not only deal out a very effective anti-tank round but also a respectable high-explosive shell. Above all this was a round, highsided turret mounting a 37mm gun, surmounted again by a separate revolving machine-gun cupola for the commander. The tank thus stood over 10 feet high.

The British experts were unhappy about most of these features and many more. They realised that the hull-mounted gun would impose tactical limitations on the way the tank could fight and they believed, in the light of experience in France, that the cupola would soon be swept off the turret. They had no objections to riveted construction as such but they felt that the armour, generally, was too thin for such a big tank and the attention paid to splash-proofing the joints between the hull plates and around the various fittings like hatches and vision slits was insufficient. Splash is the molten lead core of a bullet which will find its way through the finest crack to burn or even blind a crewman. They felt too that only scant attention had been paid to the matter of internal stowage which came nowhere near British standards, and they did not like the concept of fitting the wireless set into the hull, instead of the turret. Neither, after their experience in France, did they like the smooth, rubber-block tracks, and they expressed doubts about the use of an air-cooled aircraft engine although it appeared to be reliable enough, as did the tough suspension system.

Dewar finally obtained permission to order 1250 M3 Medium tanks on the understanding that they would be modified, under Pratt's direction, to suit British requirements. This was agreed by the Americans since at this stage Britain was still a paying customer. However, with the long term always in view Dewar, in keeping with his belief that the British General Staff consistently underestimated the number of tanks needed, ordered 3000. He argued, in the face of protests from London, that unless this was done future orders would be at risk once mass production got underway for the US Army. This was ultimately accepted if, as London wisely anticipated, only 1500 of the M3 type need be taken when a better model subsequently entered production.

In the meantime, in September, a Matilda tank called *Grampus* which like its crew belonged to 7th RTR arrived at Aberdeen, Maryland, via Canada. The crew was commanded by a Lieutenant Knott and his men were all the very best type of British NCO of that era who, despite the fact that they also could only appear in civilian clothes,

made a lasting impression on the Americans. It was more than could be said for the tank, which was seen as cramped and seriously underpowered. Indeed the only feature that seems to have impressed them was the power traverse system for the turret, which up to that time they had not developed.

Events now slowed down for a totally different reason, the forthcoming presidential election. Although theoretically available, much of American industry was still geared to commercial production and the change to war work would involve a massive retooling programme which could only be authorised if, in the long term, it could be seen as beneficial to America's own defence requirements. Obviously the authority for this could only come from the highest level, and while their President's future hung in the balance the administration was extremely cautious. They simply could not afford to be seen by public opinion to be taking steps which might be considered provocative. Progress, which until now had looked so promising, suddenly ground to a halt.

Even so the British Tank Mission had succeeded in placing orders for M3 Mediums with the Baldwin Locomotive Company and the Pullman Standard Car Company while they were still negotiating with the Pressed Steel Car Company. They wanted to add the Lima Locomotive Company to the list of contractors too, and in an effort to persuade them the company president and his wife were invited to a dinner in Washington. Noel Coward was in the capital at this time and he was seen, by the lady in question, enjoying a cocktail with Michael Dewar. Later she approached her host with a request that the famous man might be persuaded to dine with them. Dewar agreed to try, if she would persuade her husband to build tanks for Britain!

Roosevelt was confirmed as President for a third term on 5 November 1940 and things now began to look promising. One of his first moves was to set up an Office of Production Management which would oversee all munitions production in the USA and leave him with the responsibility of deciding how it was to be dispersed. At the same time the Tank Mission took stock of the situation and discovered that orders already placed for tanks and components amounted, in round figures, to $240,000,000. This came close to swallowing the entire British gold and dollar investment in the United States so, following discussions between British and US Treasury officials, a total ban on all future orders was decreed, which came into effect shortly before Christmas. For Dewar and his team this was a disaster of some proportions. Having finally sweated through and ironed out a succession of difficulties they were now halted in their tracks for want of funds. It caused a lot of bad feeling in the USA for, as one angry senator pointed out, just at the time when American industry was ready and willing to produce everything Britain needed the orders dried up. Dewar was a businessman, and a good one, but even his attempts to

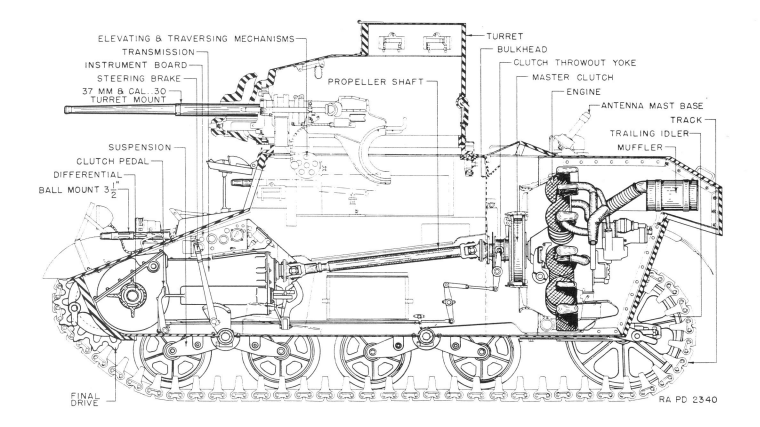

ELEVATING & TRAVERSING MECHANISMS
TRANSMISSION
INSTRUMENT BOARD
STEERING BRAKE
37 MM & CAL..30
TURRET MOUNT

PROPELLER SHAFT

TURRET
BULKHEAD
CLUTCH THROWOUT YOKE
MASTER CLUTCH
ENGINE
ANTENNA MAST BASE
TRACK
TRAILING IDLER
MUFFLER

SUSPENSION
CLUTCH PEDAL
DIFFERENTIAL
BALL MOUNT 3½"

FINAL
DRIVE

RA PD 2340

Drawing N: A cross section showing the interior of a Light Tank M3 or Stuart I as the British called it.

resolve the issue seemed to run into fresh problems at every turn. While things were sorted out he concentrated on Canada, where financial difficulties did not apply, and he also paid a visit to Clearwater, Florida, where he was taken for a trip in a new amphibious vehicle, the Roebling Alligator, which had been designed for transportation and rescue work in the swamps during the hurricane season. He was very impressed with its performance and suggested that it would form the basis for an effective amphibious tank which Britain was trying to develop at this time.

President Roosevelt was as anxious as the British to resolve the finance question and his administration came up with an answer which, if it could be made acceptable to Congress, would solve the problem at a stroke. Basically it vested the President with the authority to order any type of munitions he wished, and distribute them as he saw fit to any country that was at war with the designated aggressor nations, namely Italy and Germany, in return for certain unspecified benefits to the United States. In Britain's case this meant the use of certain strategically advantageous overseas bases. The main opposition came from congressmen and senators representing the mid-Western States where isolationism was still the dominant attitude. It became law, as the Lend-Lease Act, on 11 March 1941.

Earlier in the year Dewar was amused by an article in *Life* magazine in which the designer J Walter Christie was claiming that it was his tanks which were sweeping the British to victory in the Desert War. At the same time he was trying to persuade the Ministry of Supply, and notably his own appointee Geoffrey Burton, to accept 100 of the M2A4 light tanks pending the appearance of an improved design. The order was reduced to seventy and then ultimately to thirty-six which, due to the delay, did not arrive at their respective destinations (thirty-two to Britain and four to the Middle East) until June. Shortly after this paltry order was agreed an urgent cable arrived from Britain demanding 200 more! By the time this order was fulfilled the M2A4 had been replaced in production by the Light Tank M3 which thus formed the substance of the order.

In terms of engine, suspension and transmission the M2A4 was in many ways a scaled-down version of the medium tank. It was of riveted construction, including the high, flat-sided turret, with not a curve on it; but the seven cylinder radial engine by Continental gave it a top speed of 34 mph and again, by British standards, it was extremely reliable.

The turret mounted a 37mm gun, inferior to the 2-pounder at short range but with a better performance over longer distances. Although the gun was mounted in a fully rotating turret the gunner was able to give the weapon a few degrees of independent traverse by shoulder control without moving the turret. The few supplied to the British were used for technical assessment and familiarisation pending the arrival of the improved M3 model, the Stuart.

Now, at last, Dewar and his associates were reaping the benefit of the tremendous amount of work they had put in over the past seven months. Granted the Lend-Lease Act was none of their doing but Dewar regarded it rightly as one of the most significant events of the war for the Allies and a major defeat for Germany. And they do deserve the credit for sticking to their guns in the face of much opposition from Britain, in deciding to adopt American designs for the British Army. It enabled the Office of Production Management to form a Joint Planning Committee from members of the Ordnance Board and the British Tank Mission which could coordinate production and ensure that it went ahead as quickly and fairly as possible. The only sour note was a message from Britain

63   An M2A4 light tank with British troops in the desert—one of only four sent out there—with an M3 just beyond.

64   By November 1940 the prototype turret for the British version of the M3 Medium was ready at APG. It was fitted for trial purposes to an old M2 Medium tank.

informing Dewar that his eldest son, a fighter pilot with the RAF, was missing, presumed dead, after a patrol.

The M3 Medium pilot model was completed in March 1941 and production tanks began to appear about a month later. The first examples of the British version followed in July. In deference to British combat experience both types were more thickly armoured than originally planned – up to 50mm on the hull front – and a scheme to mount machine guns covering every angle of the hull was dropped in favour of a fixed pair mounted side by side in the front, where they proved worse than useless. Another Browning was mounted coaxially with the 37mm in the turret while the American model carried a fourth in the commander's cupola. A form of power traverse was developed for the turret while both 75mm and 37mm weapons were equipped with power stabilisers which, in theory, kept the guns steady as the tank moved over uneven ground. The British version was fitted with a cast turret, designed by L E Carr, which fitted the existing turret ring. Its general shape resembled that of the Crusader and it bulged out at the rear to provide a housing for the No 19 wireless set. It had no cupola, only a twin-flap hatch which came complete with a mounting for an anti-aircraft machine gun which British crews rarely used. Measured over the periscope this turret was four inches lower than the American one but on such a large tank this hardly made much difference. To the Ordnance Board experts the undercut sides of the British turret were an open invitation to disaster since they believed that enemy shells would be deflected downwards through the roof of the hull, but they recognised one advantage offered by the casting – the greater thickness (30mm) of the front part. Although the British clearly preferred their version it was soon apparent that in order to obtain the quantity required, both models would have to be issued to the Royal Armoured Corps. In order to distinguish between the two they were named after General Lee (for the American version) and General Grant (for the British type). Shipments to the Middle East began early in 1942 and the United States Army sent out a team of instructors to train British crews in their use. Inevitably problems arose at first, with engines that wore out rapidly in sandy conditions and suspension springs that failed consistently, but as experience grew these were overcome and in time the tank which had been so unpopular with the experts in the United Kingdom when it was first offered proved to be a great success in service.

Although they were prepared to accept the M3 Medium tank as being better than nothing in an emergency the British would certainly have preferred one that carried its main armament in a fully traversing turret, and they continued to press for this at every opportunity. A tank arranged along these lines was already being designed in Canada but it is difficult to establish to what extent, if any, this pressure had any effect. The truth, quite probably, is that it was unconscious influence at best because the

Americans seem to have come to the same conclusion sometime in 1940 when a design study for a tank to replace the M3 Medium was first discussed. Detailed design work appears to have begun in April 1941 and the British designers had been working on the Canadian tank since January. Clearly they could not be in two places at once and it would be wrong to attribute any features of the new American tank to particular British advice. Dewar was invited to inspect a wooden mock-up of the new tank, the T6, in the summer and construction of prototypes began almost at once. This tank would ultimately enter service as the M4 Medium, the Sherman. Following trials of the prototype, production began early in 1942, using the assembly line recently set up by the Lima Locomotive Works to build tanks for Britain. Thus the very first Sherman, although it carried a British War Department number and was ostensibly being built to a British contract was in fact handed over to the US Army for evaluation. This illustrates well the workings of the Lend-Lease agreement in that all obligations of contract could be ignored when occasion demanded to benefit the mutual cause. The second tank went to Britain, carrying brass nameplates with Michael engraved on them, which must have been in honour of Michael Dewar.

In addition to their important work in obtaining tanks, and the interest they had shown in the Roebling amphibian, the British Tank Mission was also responsible for ordering many other types of armoured vehicle: armoured cars, half-tracks, carriers and small airborne tanks. Since these had more impact on events during the latter half of the war they will be considered in more detail in the next volume.

The importance of the Sherman to the entire Allied war effort can hardly be overstated, and consequently it has been the subject of a number of important works. The British Army simply could not have fielded a viable tank force without it, but it is impossible to do it justice in these pages, so only a brief sketch is attempted. In respect of suspension, power unit and transmission the first two models were identical to the M3 Medium, but they differed in style of construction. The M4A1 (Sherman II to the British) was based on the design of the T6 with a cast hull while the M4 (Sherman I) had a welded hull. The M4A2 (Sherman III) also had a welded hull but was powered by a pair of General Motors diesels and was, in fact, the second version to enter production. Thus the first two types to enter British service with the Eighth Army were the cast-hulled M4A1 and the diesel-powered M4A2. Their delivery was not part of a planned programme but a response to the situation engendered by Rommel's attack on the Gazala Line. The original policy had been to issue the new tanks in small numbers to American armoured divisions for familiarisation. The USA had finally entered the war in December 1941 and was now dramatically expanding its armed forces to meet the threat from both east and west. At the same time the British were receiving

65 *The pilot M4A1 tank* Michael *arrives at Horse Guards Parade, London, on a weary old Pickfords low-loader, to be inspected by the Prime Minister.*

the balance of their orders for M3 Mediums. Churchill was in Washington conferring with Roosevelt when news of the fall of Tobruk arrived, and fears for the safety of Egypt and the canal arose once again. In response to the Prime Minister's urgent request for help General Marshall was summoned. He immediately offered to mobilise the US 2nd Armored Division, under General George S Patton, and send it to the Western Desert. Shermans were quickly gathered in from the various units to which they had been delivered but it still looked as if Egypt might be lost before Patton and his tanks arrived. It was therefore decided to deliver the tanks direct to the British Army instead, and by September 1942 over 300 had arrived in the Middle East of which some 250 were available for service at El Alamein.

Canada, like most Commonwealth countries, had given little serious thought to the manufacture of armoured fighting vehicles, or indeed military vehicles of any kind, between the wars. They were content to obtain a few light tanks and carriers from Great Britain for training purposes and relied on civilian-type trucks for their basic needs. Yet there was always the enthusiast who managed to generate enough interest to get the odd project started and at least one six-wheeled armoured car, copied from a British design, was tested in Canada before the war.

The presence of a British Supply Mission in Canada, almost from the outbreak of war, has already been mentioned. Its initial interest in tanks was limited to components, but after the fall of France consideration was given to the construction of complete machines, and the model chosen was the Valentine. It was a sensible choice. The type was only just entering service with the British Army but it was clearly going to be a reliable vehicle, relatively straightforward to assemble, while many of its components, such as suspension units, transmission assemblies and General Motors diesel engines were already being manufactured in the United States and could easily be diverted to Canada.

Even so it was not all plain sailing. The Canadians had no established tank-building plants and there was an initial delay in the supply of working drawings from Britain. The first problem was overcome by the adaptation of the Angus Works in Montreal of the Canadian Pacific Railway Company but the drawings, when they finally arrived, had to be completely reworked to suit Canadian engineering practice, and this caused considerable delay. An initial order for 300 Valentines was placed, based on the British Mark IV model which featured the GM engine, two-man turret and 2-pounder gun with a coaxial Besa. This last was soon changed for the more readily obtainable Browning machine-gun, while other modifications to suit the tank to local production included the use of armour castings for certain parts, notably the hull nose-plates and turrets. Delays at various stages meant that the first production models did not appear until the summer of 1941, but from then on things improved. British experts visiting Canada learned of problems with the supply of armour plate and it soon became clear that the Canadians were moving away from the idea of adding orders for Valentines to be used by their own army. Nevertheless from these small beginnings Canadian industry managed to produce over 1400 Valentines Marks VI, VII (which had many detail improvements), and VIIA (which had long-range fuel tanks and special tracks for use on ice). The majority were supplied to Russia to honour British obligations made when that country was invaded by Germany in June 1941.

A scheme was also afoot to produce the A15 Crusader in Canada and a sample tank was sent out from Britain for examination. But through their contacts with the British Tank Mission and US Ordnance Board the Canadians were soon showing a greater interest in the M3 Medium, although in a cable to London dated 16 September 1940, General Pakenham-Walsh stated 'as regards Canadian production we consider A15 a better article than M3 and should prefer Canada to make it.' The Canadians knew better, and so did Dewar. He saw in their preference an ideal way of overcoming apparent American reluctance to build an effective turreted tank instead of the M3 and, early in 1941, despatched Carr to Ottawa to discuss the possibilities. He was aided in this by a shortage of armour plate in Canada, which was already affecting Valentine production and causing the Americans to limit the supply of components for tanks that might never get built. Following discussions with Colonel William Mavor, the Canadian Army liaison officer in Washington, Carr designed a form of cast hull which would accept a larger turret and fit onto the existing M3 underframe. This hull was not only easier for Canada to produce, it turned out to be a good deal lower and better armoured than the original M3.

Production lines were set up in the Montreal Locomotive Works and the new tank was nicknamed Ram, apparently derived from the family crest of General F F

66 Canadian built Valentines, still awaiting their 2-pounder guns, take part in a small parade for workers and visitors at the Canadian Pacific works in Montreal.

67 An overhead view of the pilot model Ram cruiser tank showing the side hull doors and auxiliary Browning machine-gun turret.

Worthington, commander of the Canadian armour. Since it was never used operationally as a fighting tank the Ram has received far less attention than it deserves. In many respects it was a good deal more advanced than its British and American contemporaries but it also exhibited some outmoded features. These included side doors in the hull, which were eliminated in the Sherman at the prototype stage, and an auxiliary machine-gun turret at the front which was probably incorporated as a sop to ruling British preferences. The Ram was designed at the outset to mount the 6-pounder gun but this was not available when the first fifty-five tanks were being built, so they mounted a 2-pounder instead. The one-piece cast turret was fitted with a bolt-on front plate which held the mantlet so that, in theory, it was possible to exchange weapon mountings. This made it one of the first Allied tanks to have the ability to up-gun built into the design. Production began towards the end of 1941 and by early 1942 the first 6-pounder model, the Ram II, entered production. Subsequent modifications included elimination of the side

68 *The original Hamilton Bridge armoured car was a huge vehicle with a pitiful armament.*

69 *The second Canadian armoured car mounted a 2-pounder and, with its free-rolling spare wheels would have had a good cross-country performance had it not been for the bulbous nose.*

doors and front turret, the latter being replaced by a conventional hull machine-gun mounting.

Soon after the war began another armoured vehicle appeared in Canada bearing all the hallmarks of inexperience. it consisted of a bulky armoured body mounted on an International Harvester lorry chassis. This was surmounted by a large machine-gun turret and above that again was an octagonal cupola. The armouring was carried out by the Hamilton Bridge Company in Ontario, who are believed to have been one of the few industrial organisations in the country to have some experience of welding on a large scale. Certainly the armoured car appears to have been welded and only flat plates were used in its construction. All the same its cross-country performance would have been poor and its armament, for such a large vehicle, rather puny. It was followed by a second car in which the designer had sought to overcome these problems without, it seems, doing anything to improve its appearance. The new armoured car was a four wheeler but extra wheels were carried, clear of the ground,

between the roadwheels on each side. They would have been mounted on free-rolling stub axles so that the car could not belly, or strand itself on obstacles. These wheels could also double as spares in the event of a puncture. The hull itself was quite low and well-shaped, being formed from flat welded panels, while the turret, which mounted a 2-pounder gun, was rather like a small Crusader tank turret but with vision slots all round which obviated the need for a cupola. So far the car looked quite good, had an effective armament and, potentially, a reasonable cross-country performance; but this last was spoiled by the transmission housing, a large casting which stuck out at the front and would have effectively prevented the car from tackling a steep bank.

Since armoured cars would be required from Canadian factories, and these homemade designs were clearly not suitable, fresh orders were placed for a range of vehicles based on British ideas. These included a light reconnaissance car, a scout car and an armoured car. The last two were not completed for service until 1943, and will be examined later, but the first type appeared in 1942. It was known as the Otter, but any similarity with British vehicles of the same type, like the Humber L R C, was limited to the tiny Bren gun turret. This sat on top of a bulky armoured hull, again built by the Hamilton Bridge Company, which in turn rested on a General Motors four-wheel drive chassis. Some 1700 were built, the majority of which saw service with armoured car companies of the R A F and R C A F. Although rather large for the work they had to do, and consequently heavy and underpowered, they seem to have been popular on account of their reliability. Canada was also involved in the British plan to build a really big eight-wheeled armoured car for desert operations, and a prototype was built by Ford. Many legends surround this vehicle; that it was built more or less unofficially following a conversation in a Quebec bar, and that the gearbox was fitted in such a way that the vehicle had one forward speed and four in reverse. These may be no more than a smokescreen to disguise what was, in fact, a bad design. There was clearly a British requirement for such a vehicle and at least four different types were built, all of which proved to be unsuccessful, but the Canadian version gives an impression of being the best-looking of the lot. Irrespective of whether the gearbox was installed the wrong way round or not it drove to all eight wheels, and steering appears to have been on the first and last axle. The hull, which was of both riveted and welded construction, was low compared with its rivals, and shaped in a way that suggests its designers had some knowledge of the big German armoured cars that it was intended to match. The cast turret, with bolted front plate and 2-pounder gun looks like a close copy of the Ram tank design, if not an actual Ram turret.

Canada was also drawn into the Universal Carrier programme and soon became a major supplier. Mass production got underway early in 1941 and continued

70   A large herd of Otter light reconnaissance cars wave their Bren guns harmlessly at a passing aircraft. Bulky as they were Otters proved to be popular and reliable vehicles.

71   Marmon-Herrington Mark II armoured cars of the Royals. They mount Boys rifles and Vickers machine-guns, the latter on the rear of the turret.

72   A South African manned Marmon-Herrington in East Africa. It is a Mark III in MFF configuration, mounting a Vickers gun in the turret.

throughout the war, the carriers being built at the Ford Plant in Windsor, Ontario with armoured hulls supplied by the Dominion Bridge Co at Sandwich, in the same province. The Canadian carriers were very similar to their British counterparts, the only differences being of a minor nature in order to suit them to Canadian manufacturing processes.

During the early stages of the war in the Middle East the British discussed the possibility of establishing a large tank supply and repair facility at Port Elizabeth in South Africa, but it foundered on fears expressed in some quarters that if the general war situation in Africa deteriorated beyond a certain point the South Africans might be tempted to use the establishment for their own purposes to the detriment of British interests. In fact the South African government had been investigating the possibility of building armoured-car bodies, to fit on imported chassis, since 1937, and when war broke out this assumed a greater degree of importance. Work then began on the design of what came to be known as the South African Reconnaissance Car, based on a Ford V8 3-ton lorry chassis. It was a relatively cumbersome design with a large, wide body supporting a drum-shaped turret. Vickers machine-guns were mounted in the turret and, for some strange reason, on the left side of the hull, while two large access doors were provided at the rear. It was soon appreciated that four-wheel drive would be more appropriate for such a vehicle and investigations revealed that the Marmon-Herrington Company of Indianapolis, USA, produced what amounted to a conversion kit that permitted the Ford chassis to be fitted with a driven front-axle. It took some time to arrange for delivery of these items so the Mark I model continued in production almost until the end of 1940, when the Mark II appeared. There has always been a tendency to refer to all South African armoured cars as Marmon-Herringtons although, of course, this was meaningless in the case of the Mark I. The Mark II was almost identical in terms of outward appearance although there was a gradual change to welded construction at an early stage. It also appeared in two forms; the Mobile Field Force (MFF) model for the Union Defence Force, which carried the same armament as the Mark I, and the Middle East (ME) model issued for use by Allied forces in that theatre which carried Bren and Boys guns instead. Over 1000 examples of all three types were produced, a considerable achievement for a country which industrially was relatively undeveloped.

It soon became clear that a better model was needed, preferably with thicker armour, but in order to achieve this on the existing chassis it was vital to reduce the overall size. The redesign resulted not only in a more compact and better-shaped body but a shorter wheelbase, which still retained the Marmon-Herrington four-wheel drive capability and enhanced the cross-country performance. Designated Mark III, it also appeared in MFF and ME

73 An up-gunned Marmon-Herrington Mark II with its turret replaced, in this case, by a German 37mm anti-tank gun and a Vickers on a pedestal at the back.

74 The huge and ugly Albion eight-wheeled armoured car nearing completion in the workshops. The size may be estimated from the man working on the front axle.

75 The prototype Indian wheeled carrier serves as a backdrop to an alarming display of military fashion!

variants but the armament, in either case, was now concentrated in the turret. Over 2000 were built before production ended in the summer of 1942 and these excellent cars saw extensive service all over Africa, the Middle and Far East. Many famous British regiments owe a considerable degree of their modern reputations to successes gained in these cars and they seem to have been very popular.

The term reconnaissance car, as coined in Britain, meant something between a scout car and a full blown armoured car, although the distinctions are blurred. In any case, with armoured warfare, it has always proved difficult to control the circumstances under which the various vehicles are used. Inevitably vehicles can get into situations which demand more, in terms of protection or firepower, than they have been designed for. If they survive the experience the crew, just as inevitably, will ask for improvements to both and the situation can easily escalate until it gets out of hand. The Marmon-Herringtons serve as a good example. In the desert, where territory and equipment changed hands on a regular basis, the British Army soon found itself with an appreciable stock of captured weapons which were pounced on by the armoured-car crews with great delight. Before long Marmon-Herringtons of Marks II and III could be found all over the desert with their turrets replaced by a variety of weapons ranging from Italian Breda 20mm cannon to German 37mm anti-tank guns or even French and British pieces of similar calibre. One car had a battery of Bren guns mounted on the side of the hull for anti-aircraft defence while others were modified as transport for Light Aid Detachments who might have to repair vehicles on the battlefield.

It has already been recorded how with the arrival of the Germans in North Africa the British were alarmed by reports of enormous eight-wheeled armoured cars that could roam the desert at high speed, destroying everything in their path. The Canadian eight-wheeler was one attempt to counter this supposed threat, while another was built in the United States and two in South Africa. One of these falls within the period under review. It was known as the South African Heavy Armoured Car Mark V and it began life as a test chassis, running on eight wheels of which only the four centre ones were driven, the outer set at each end being used for support and steering only. In its original form the huge car was powered by two Albion six-cylinder engines, one at each end, but performance trials proved that it was incapable of negotiating soft sand, which was its object. Despite this failing it was rebuilt by the South African Railways workshop near Johannesburg with the two engines mounted side by side at the back and an armoured body. The revised layout gave the vehicle an extremely long hull but at least it left some room at the front for a crew compartment and sizeable turret, which was intended to carry a 6-pounder gun. The big car was well armoured, even by contemporary tank standards:

76 *The second version of the Borbette anti-tank vehicle with its wooden mock-up body on a short wheelbase Canadian chassis.*

77 *Another mock-up: the Indian designed Chevrolet personnel carrier. The machine-gun mounting above the cab is hidden by the shadows from the tree.*

reports speak of 40mm thick plate at the front reducing to 20mm at the sides, but in keeping with a contemporary obsession large skirting plates were fitted which all but covered the wheels. These were made in segments capable of being swung upwards for servicing or tyre changing, but they did nothing to reduce the weight which stood at 16 tons. Clearly this was out of the question, especially in a vehicle which already had a poor performance on desert terrain, so after a brief period when it was hoped to redesign it into a self-propelled artillery mount it was discarded. The other eight wheeler and subsequent four-wheeler developments will be covered in the next volume.

When the tank situation was at its most desperate in Britain, in June 1940, General Pope put forward two suggestions which, on the face of it, seemed fantastic. The first was to order tanks from Russia. In the light of subsequent events it is probably just as well that this was not pursued, for within little more than a year Britain was actually supplying tanks to the Soviet Union. Pope's other idea was to build them in India. Reports from that country indicated that they had the industrial resources to construct armoured hulls and manufacture tracks but everything else would have to be imported. Cadillac engines were known to be available from the United States but before any further details could be settled the idea was dropped. All the same there was no intention of wasting India's resources and plans were drawn up for the production of wheeled armoured vehicles. The first of these was a species of carrier on a Ford/Marmon-Herrington chassis. Built by the Tata Iron and Steel Works, they looked like large, misshapen scout cars with the engine at the front and an open-top fighting compartment. The long bonnet was covered by horizontal metal strips acting as splash rails to deflect small-arms fire away from the driver's visor, but the martial effect was somewhat spoiled by the original Ford chrome trimmed headlamps and the dome-shaped hub caps. Production was limited to ten vehicles which were only used for training purposes in India. The Mark II, which appeared in 1942, was used on active service in North Africa and Italy. It was built in various forms including an armoured observation vehicle which sported a small turret. The chassis of the Mark II was a Canadian Ford, converted to rear engine layout and fitted with four-wheel drive. Conventional front-engined versions of the same chassis were used for prototypes of a 2-pounder equipped tank destroyer called the Borbette. This featured an armoured cab and, in the Mark I version, an anti-tank gun with armoured shield on a turntable at the back. The Mark II had a shorter wheelbase and the gun, which faced to the rear, was housed in an extension of the cab which meant that it was unable to traverse. Neither type was developed to production status.

Armoured cars had been built in India as early as 1915, in answer to the problems caused by a shortage of manpower. While large numbers of men were serving overseas dissident elements at home took advantage of the situation to create trouble and the primitive cars were employed to offset the weakness of the remaining troops. Few details are available of a Chevrolet-based armoured personnel-carrier – there are only two photographs, one of which is shown here. The body is fully protected and well provided with loopholes through which the infantry passengers could use their rifles. There is a raised conning tower at the front with a Vickers machine-gun mounted. It was probably intended for use in urban areas to deal with rioters. Another potential trouble area was the North West Frontier, as it had been ever since anyone could remember.

Late in 1938 Major D H J Williams, commanding the South Waziristan Scouts, ordered panels of bulletproof plate, and when they arrived about a month before the war began, he fitted them to some of the unit's 1937

78 One of the protected Chevrolet trucks of the South Waziristan Scouts, still sporting chromed front bumper bar and grille.

Chevrolet trucks. What he ended up with was a sort of armoured bus capable of carrying troops or stores. Most of the protection was limited to the cab and body, and large, hinged panels were used to close off the windscreen and side openings if the vehicle came under fire. The bodies were later transferred to newer (1939 model) Chevrolet chassis but when six more were required in 1940 no more bulletproof plate was available. Williams therefore settled for mild steel instead but he used two layers with a narrow air gap between which, he found, would stop a .303 inch bullet at point-blank range. Plate was now also fitted to the sides of the bonnet and a light machine-gun mounting was added to the roof. Trying to knock the lorries out became something of a sport with the Mahsud tribesmen and Williams recorded about sixty hits on vehicles in one year for a return of four slightly wounded among the scouts. When the unit was issued with a few artillery pieces – 13-pounder field guns and 4.5 inch howitzers, in 1939 a gun-carrying truck was designed. There were too few guns to equip every post and they were not up to being towed behind the trucks, so the trucks provided the necessary mobility. Only the front end of each vehicle was armoured, the rest being open, but the guns could not be fired from the lorry. Detachable ramps were therefore provided so that they could be quickly dismounted and brought into action as required.

Despite its size, in terms of land area, Australia was not well endowed with heavy industry when the war began but it more than made up for it with enthusiasm and ingenuity. A few armoured cars had been built on Ford truck chassis before the war and in 1939 a Mark 3 version was in production. It was a cumbersome, turreted vehicle mounting a single machine gun and this was followed, in 1940, by the Mark 4 which featured the Marmon-Herrington four-wheel drive system. On this model the turret was little more than an armoured shield. At least one armoured car of the Home Guard type was also built but very little is known about it. Australia's tank force at this time consisted of a few obsolete British models but it soon

79 *Australian built Dingo scout cars leading a column of Sentinel tanks during a War Loan parade in Melbourne.*

capabilities of existing industry. The first of these was a Ford/Marmon-Herrington-based scout car. It was named Dingo, after the native wild dog, but should not be confused with the British Daimler, which it did not resemble in the slightest. The Australian Dingo was quite large as scout cars go and of conventional layout with a front-mounted engine and open top compartment for a crew of two. It could carry a Bren gun or Boys anti-tank rifle but was extremely uncomfortable to drive, and although built in some numbers it never saw service overseas.

Tracked carriers were another type that Australia had the resources to build and their first model was based on the layout of the British Bren Carrier. In order to simplify production the track displacement steering system was not used and lever operated brake steering was used instead. Known as the LP1 – for Local Production – it was normally seen mounting the water-cooled Vickers machine-gun. It was soon followed into production by the LP2 which was based on the Universal Carrier and did employ the wheel-operated Vickers steering system, and by the LP2A which had a revised internal layout to allow a radio set to be fitted. Carriers of this type were produced in quite large numbers and remained with the Australian

became clear that further deliveries from the United Kingdom could not be expected for some time. However, as Australia was such a long way from the war there appeared to be no great urgency to acquire them, except for training, and in the meantime it was decided to develop various lighter types of armoured vehicle which were within the

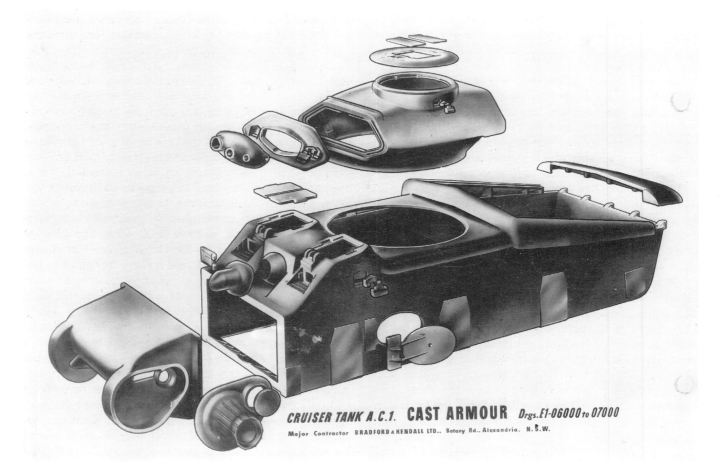

CRUISER TANK A.C.1. CAST ARMOUR Drgs. E1-06000 to 07000

Major Contractor BRADFORD & KENDALL LTD., Botany Rd., Alexandria. N.S.W.

80 *A manufacturer's diagram showing the various castings which go to make up an Australian Cruiser (Sentinel) tank.*

Army long enough to see some active service during the Korean War.

The very suggestion that Australia could produce its own tanks was greeted with a good deal of scepticism in that country when it was first put forward, and with virtual disbelief when it was mentioned in Britain or the United States. On the other hand, with the situation in Britain getting worse almost by the day, it was quite clear that it was the only chance Australia had of getting tanks at all in the immediate future. In addition to being desperately short of adequate heavy engineering facilities there was no one in the country with any experience of tank design and construction at all. The most positive aspects of the situation were the determination and almost naive confidence of the engineers who were not aware that it could not be done. The problem of manufacture could be overcome by the intelligent use of available resources and the lack of expertise was alleviated by the loan, from Britain, of Colonel W D Watson, a senior member of the Mechanisation Board who arrived late in 1940 after a stopover in the United States. While there he met an Australian engineer, Mr A Chamberlain, who was investigating the tank situation in America, and both men agreed that the M3 Medium tank should form the basis of whatever was built in Australia.

The problems that faced the design team were prodigious. To the usual difficulties of official prevarication and endless minor changes which plagued tank builders everywhere were added the immense problems of production and supply, especially of imported items. Provision of armour plate was the greatest problem of all. It was not that Australia was incapable of producing rolled plate of the type required for tank construction, it was simply that production facilities were already committed beyond the foreseeable future. The suggestion was therefore put forward that the design of the new tank should be based on a series of castings which could be bolted together, like the British Matilda. It was then asked why the entire hull of the tank could not be cast as a single unit, and the turret likewise. It was a drastic step – before then only the French had succeeded in producing complex armour castings of similar size, and their experience was unobtainable. Undeterred, the metallurgists from the steel industry set out to develop a suitable compound and, in doing so, probably exceeded even their own expectations. They produced a hull with a maximum frontal thickness of 45mm and a turret of 65mm which, from comparative tests, was found to be on a par with, if not better than, similar structures produced in Britain and the United States in its ability to resist anti-tank fire. It was the perfection of this technique which gave the Australian Cruiser Mark I (ACI) – or Sentinel as it came to be called – its distinctive shape.

If Watson's original scheme had proved possible this hull would have been mounted on the transmission and running gear of the American M3, but even this ideal could not be achieved. The demand for engines and gearboxes in the United States was such that none could be spared for Australia and once again the engineers were called in. A complex synchromesh gearbox was beyond the capacity of local industry so a five-speed crash box was developed instead, incorporating controlled differential steering. Since no engine of a similar size and output was available an ingenious design, using three Cadillac model 75 engines of V8 configuration, was adopted instead. In order to get all three into the hull they were installed two abreast with the third behind, on the centre line. Drive-shafts from all three passed into a transfer box beneath the turret from which a single cardan shaft delivered the power to the front-mounted gearbox. Although this system posed the usual problems of synchronisation and increased servicing time the combined unit delivered 330 brake horsepower which gave the prototype a top speed of 40 mph, governed down to 30 mph in production machines. When it came to the matter of suspension the American system was abandoned in favour of one based on the French Hotchkiss type. This may have been due to the arrival in Australia of a French engineer, R Perrier. He had been working in Japan on behalf of the French government but left that country in a hurry when the situation in the Pacific deteriorated in 1941. In the end the only items that Sentinel shared in common with the American tank were the style of roadwheel and the rubber block, double-pin track.

Obviously at this stage the only available tank gun was the 2-pounder, which was mounted along with a coaxial .303 Vickers machine-gun in the turret while another Vickers was located in the hull front, protected by a somewhat vulgar-looking casting. Although it was never subjected to the ultimate test of battle there is little reason to doubt that in its day the Sentinel stood comparison with any Allied and most contemporary enemy tanks. Yet it had been designed, almost from scratch, and produced in prototype form in a little less than a year. Even so, about halfway through that year it had come close to being rejected because of the many difficulties anticipated in its production. When Chamberlain arrived home from the United States he submitted another design, known as the AC2, which would have been a lighter type based more closely on American components. This was rejected once the problems of obtaining these parts was fully appreciated, and the AC1 was restored to favour. The first prototype was ready in January 1942 and was soon followed by two more. That weaknesses showed up during trials was hardly surprising but none of them were of a terminal nature. Roadwheel tyres wore out at an alarming rate and the locally designed electric turret traverse refused to function if the tank was standing on a slope. Cooling, too, proved to be inadequate. These faults could be remedied but mass production remained a problem. Parts for the three prototypes had to be produced at workshops in different parts of the country and then brought together

81 *Three AC1 Sentinel tanks on an exercise in the bush.*

for assembly. Clearly if it was to enter production it was desirable to organise a proper assembly line, so while development of the prototypes went ahead a brand new factory was being built at Chullora in New South Wales. From this plant the first production Sentinel emerged in August 1942, and sixty-six were built before production switched to a new model.

If, early in the war, Australia had seemed to be an unlikely place to produce armoured vehicles New Zealand would have appeared to be downright impossible. To those in the Northern Hemisphere the country seemed to be little more than a couple of offshore islands of its huge western neighbour and this attitude, coupled with a perfectly understandable national pride, was probably one of the main reasons why New Zealand chose, as far as possible, to achieve something on its own. Unlike in Australia, virtually no attempt had been made to mechanise the New Zealand Army at all before the war. Yet the subject had been seriously considered in a paper written in 1938, and the writer had even drawn attention to a strange species of tank built by the Disston Tractor Company in the United States. This amounted to nothing more than a turreted, armoured hull which, with little modification, could be fitted onto a Caterpillar-type crawler tractor to produce a rudimentary kind of tank. A few had even been sold to the Afghan Army.

Nevertheless the authorities in New Zealand were not considering the production of tanks at all. They had received some Bren Carriers from Britain and confidently expected a small delivery of tanks in a short while. Thus, for the present, they concentrated on improvised wheeled armoured-vehicles and commenced experiments with a Bedford lorry, the cab of which was replaced by an open-top crew compartment and protected bonnet. It carried one Lewis gun. This was followed by a hideously ugly armoured Ford with a gabled roof which looked no more convincing than some of the Home Guard vehicles then being built in Britain. It was succeeded by a much more professional product which was clearly based on the early version of the British Beaverette. The New Zealand model was a good deal bigger, being based on a 30 cwt Ford truck chassis but for all that only carried a crew of two armed with a Bren gun and Boys anti-tank rifle. The armour was mostly obtained from Australia and over 200 were built.

Once Australia began to build her own carriers the New Zealand government assumed that it would be able to obtain some, but even this plan came to nothing. By mid 1940 it was decided that arrangements would have to be made to produce carriers in New Zealand and the railway workshops at Hutt Valley in North Island was selected as the contractor. The first model, of which forty were built, was a close copy of the British Bren Carrier, even down to the steering system, but they had to be constructed from mild steel plate since no armour could be obtained from Australia. The next model was based on the Austra-

82 *The prototype New Zealand version of the Beaverette was a ramshackle looking specimen even when it was new.*

lian LP2 – indeed it was virtually identical – and it was built from proper armour plate from the same source. An LP2A version also appeared, and in all some 900 examples of both types were completed and entered service with the New Zealand Army in the homeland and on Fiji.

Hopes of obtaining any British tanks were dashed by events in Europe in June 1940, so the idea of obtaining some of the Disston Tractor Tanks was revived. The Public Works Department was approached concerning the availability of suitable Caterpillar tractors, and after studying details they announced that they could see no great difficulty in building the whole thing from local resources instead. The idea obviously appealed to the government who instructed the PWD to build a wooden mock-up which was soon followed by a mild-steel prototype. Caterpillar D8 tractors were available in fairly large numbers so one of these formed the chassis. It was covered all over by an armoured shell and topped off with a small turret, which gave the tank an awe-inspiring height of 12 feet. Attempts to improve the performance in terms of speed and cross-country performance failed on both counts and the chassis was ultimately returned to something approaching its original form. Known as Bob Semple tanks in honour of a government minister supposedly responsible for their introduction, three were built before it became apparent that the entire scheme was going to be a resounding flop. A shortage of more suitable weapons meant that each tank carried a total of six Bren guns; two facing forward, one in each side, another at the rear and the sixth in the small turret on top. The supply of armour plate was a problem which was only partly solved by the curious expedient of covering most of the body with a form of corrugated plate which was expected to deflect bullets if it could not actually resist them. Each tank required a crew of eight including a driver whose seat had been removed from the back, along with the controls, to a forward position alongside the engine. Yet

83 *Crowds part in awe as a 'Bob Semple' improvised tank comes rumbling down the road during a military parade in Auckland.*

84 *Looking down upon the second version of the Schofield tank. This picture, taken when the tank was in Britain, shows it in the wheeled mode.*

even he was not as uncomfortable as the crew member who operated the central, front-mounted Bren gun: he had to lie face downwards on a mattress placed over the engine. The original plan had been to keep the armoured hulls in store at strategic locations around the country to be mounted on to the tractors in the event of a Japanese invasion. But the scheme was clearly impractical and became the subject of public ridicule when the tanks took part in some parades, so it was soon dropped.

At about the same time as the Bob Semple tank project was getting underway a motor vehicle dealer from Auckland, E J Schofield, approached the New Zealand government with a tank project of his own. Based on the chassis of a General Motors (Chevrolet) truck it was of rather bizarre appearance and included a feature which had been popular in Britain some twenty years earlier. This was the wheel-cum-track concept which described a vehicle designed to run on tracks or wheels as conditions required. It never proved practical even on professionally designed vehicles, and Schofield's effort was both untidy and ill conceived; it failed miserably on trials. A crew of three was carried; driver and hull machine-gunner behind the front-mounted engine, and another machine-gunner in a rear-mounted turret which was based on a pre-war Vickers light tank design. Tracks and suspension components were of the Universal Carrier type, supported by an outside girder frame and protected by moveable steel skirting-plates. This frame was used to elevate the tracks when the tank ran on wheels but these had first to be removed from stowage points on the hull and bolted to their hubs before the tank could drive away.

Although it proved incapable of passing any test that involved cross-country operation, and despite a good deal of adverse comment from American, Australian and British experts, the New Zealand government pressed on with an improved version which, although it was always known as the Schofield tank, was in fact the work of other mem-

bers of his team. Heeding a comment from a British officer that a mobile anti-tank gun was the ideal type of fighting vehicle for New Zealand, the new model carried a 2-pounder gun in a small, open-top turret, but it still retained the wheel-cum-track capability. Indeed it was a much more balanced design, properly engineered and well built, although by the time it was completed late in 1942 sufficient tanks had arrived from Britain and the USA to serve New Zealand's immediate needs. Again carrier components were used for the tracks and suspension and a Chevrolet engine was fitted, but the transmission, obtained from Marmon-Herrington, was much more robust. In 1943 the little tank was despatched to Britain where it appears to have been received with very little interest. It was displayed on Horse Guards Parade in London and even evaluated by the Department of Tank Design, and their conclusions were by no means all unfavourable. However their recommendation was that the project be dropped, although the tank remained stored with other derelicts at a compound in Chertsey until after the war, when it was scrapped.

It remains to record briefly certain other armoured vehicles built under British supervision in various parts of the world which could not be described correctly as parts of the Empire, at least not in all cases. The Sudan Defence Force, which came into existence between the wars, was suddenly vested with immense responsibilities when the Italian threat materialised in Eritrea. Attached British officers and NCOs of the Royal Army Service Corps decided to supplement the force's two vintage Rolls-Royce armoured cars and Ford pick-up trucks with a homemade design on Ford 30 cwt chassis. The result was a large, spartan-looking vehicle, of which forty-five were built, which mounted a Bren gun and Boys anti-tank rifle in a low open turret. The cars were issued to the Motor Machine Gun Companies of the SDF and operated alongside the Ford pick-ups, each of which mounted a Vickers

85 *Two of the rugged looking Ford armoured cars of the Sudan Defence Force. The crews are wearing British pattern tank helmets and even their boots on this occasion.*

machine-gun. Apart from the fact that Sudanese troops preferred to drive in bare feet rather than use the boots that were issued, the cars proved extremely useful and saw action even in the rough Eritrean hill-country, where at least some were fitted with wire-mesh turret roofs to keep out handgrenades.

The East African Reconnaissance Regiment, based in Kenya, started the war with a fleet of unarmoured International trucks, mounting Bren guns, which were used to patrol roads close to the Ethiopian frontier. They were replaced in 1940 by a series of locally designed armoured cars based on Chevrolet chassis. They came in three types; 'Susies' which were turretless, and 'Eydes' and 'Fortesses' which mounted small turrets. They were assembled in Nairobi, using boiler plate in lieu of real armour, and employed during the advance on Addis Ababa. In due course the unit was renamed the East African Armoured Car Regiment and the improvised cars were replaced by South African built Marmon-Herringtons.

In the troubled regions north of the Suez Canal locally built armoured vehicles were used by a number of forces under some form of British control. The Transjordan Frontier Force had been operating armed, if not armoured, vehicles for many years and numbers were still in service during the war. In Palestine the Arab Legion also fielded a Desert Mechanised Force which originally used pick-up trucks and open-top Ford armoured cars of a type also operated by the Palestine Police. Under the aggressive command of Colonel J B Glubb the Legion's area of operations was enlarged to assist British forces trying to contain trouble spots as far away as Syria and Iraq, so it was decided to produce more substantial armoured vehicles. A large shipment of Ford truck chassis

was obtained from the United States and fitted with locally built bodies made from two layers of mild steel plate separated by a layer of plywood which proved sufficiently bulletproof. The large turrets mounted a Vickers machine-gun and Boys anti-tank rifle, while a Lewis gun was carried for anti-aircraft protection. Two or three different models were produced, some of which had an open crew compartment at the back.

86 *An Eyde type armoured car of the East African Armoured Car regiment during the advance on Addis Ababa. The extra springs stowed on the side suggest that the armour was a bit much for the Chevrolet chassis over bush roads.*

87   *A Ford based armoured car of the Arab Legion in a typical desert setting, complete with fort.*

7 To El Alamein and back

88 *Under the guns of a German tank, from which the picture was taken, a British crewman scrambles to escape from a burning Crusader.*

Casualties are inevitable in war, and acceptable to the average soldier within limits if he can justify what he is fighting for. But some forms of death are especially horrifying and, to the tank man, the worst by far is to be burned, trapped inside your tank. There is some comfort in statistics and during the Second World War these tend to show that men fighting from within armoured vehicles had a better chance of survival than the unprotected footsoldier. This apparent comfort, however, is apt to evaporate very quickly when one sees a tank burst into flames before all the crew have had a chance to bale out. Reports from the desert battles of 1941 showed that, with British tanks at any rate, this was happening far too often, and efforts were made to discover the reason.

To the uninformed it seemed obvious that the problem was caused by petrol from ruptured fuel tanks, but on closer examination it became clear that fires were just as common in diesel tanks, while German machines, which were all powered by petrol engines, seldom took fire. Once a tank had been engulfed in flames it was all but impossible for even the most painstaking investigator to tell exactly where the fire started, so a number of damaged tanks were towed out into the desert, stocked up with ammunition and fuel and then shot at. The report compiled by the officers concerned makes interesting reading, not least for its anecdotal style, but it also reached some interesting conclusions. Fires, it seemed, could be started by electrical wires being severed and shorting out, or by badly stowed kit like an oil-soaked greatcoat rolled up and stuffed under the driver's seat, which would smoulder and flare up after a piece of shot lodged in it. But the most common and devastating cause proved to be ammunition. Red hot splinters from a penetrating shell would ignite the cordite of a single round and turn the fighting compartment into an inferno in seconds as other stowed ammunition went up. Now it was clear why the problem had not been observed to anything like the same extent in German tanks. They carried their ammunition in lightly armoured bins, so that even if the odd round went off, it did not automatically spread to the rest. When, in time, the British adopted this practice the situation improved dramatically.

No matter how desperate his situation might appear, one thing it was important never to give Rommel was time. This is something that neither Wavell nor Auchinleck seem to have appreciated. Whether General Pope, who was nominated to command 30 Corps shortly before Crusader was launched, would have been more perceptive will never be known; he was killed in an air crash early in October on the way to the front and was replaced by the less experienced General Norrie. By January 1942 Auchinleck was so firm in his conviction that the Germans would not be capable of launching a new offensive in the immediate future that he scheduled his own next move, towards Tripoli, for mid-February. In the meantime the newly arrived 2nd Armoured Brigade of 1st Armoured Division came forward to relieve the survivors of Crusader. Its three regiments, the Bays, 9th Lancers and 10th Hussars fielded one squadron of Stuarts to two of Crusaders, but they had a long drive behind them and lacked the desert experience to deal with Rommel. In addition they had just had a change of commander, when General Lumsden, wounded in an air attack, was replaced by General Messervy. Rommel too had been reinforced with a further fifty-five machines which effectively doubled his tank strength if one ignores the Italians (as almost everyone did).

Rommel made his move on 21 January although he soon had the Italian War Minister breathing down his neck, counselling caution. Indeed, this worthy refused to allow his troops to move east of Agedabia, so the Afrika Korps went on alone. Two days later it encountered elements of 2nd Armoured Brigade which had split up to answer calls for help from other retreating units. This was meat and drink to Rommel who almost destroyed 9th Lancers and 10th Hussars in separate actions. The next move effectively fooled the British command and led 8th RTR, who were covering Benghazi, to undertake a series of long night moves, first one way and then the other, until even their reliable Valentines were showing signs of wear, not to mention their crews. Benghazi was recaptured by the Germans on 29 January while Rommel, with a smaller force, moved directly east to occupy Msus as the scattered British forces hurried eastwards as best they could. By 4 February the Germans had nearly ground to a halt, having outstripped their supply lines, and the British were settling in on what became known as the Gazala Line. Here they would remain, taking time out to raid and skirmish, for the next four months.

The Gazala Line was not the imposing edifice that its name suggests, but more a fragmented series of strong-points, or 'boxes', protected by minefields, which ran for about fifty miles on a roughly south-easterly bearing from Gazala on the coast to Bir Hacheim. It was not best suited to defence since Auchinleck regarded it more as a jumping-off point for his next proposed offensive, and in any case its southern flank lay wide-open to the desert. Furthermore, and in spite of repeated demands from London, the 'Auk' had no intention of moving until his own force had been substantially strengthened. He had, in particular, two new pieces of equipment to look forward to. One was the General Grant tank, which would be issued first to 3rd RTR. The other was the 6-pounder anti-tank gun, just beginning to arrive in substantial numbers.

The subject of anti-tank guns has only been touched upon and this might be a suitable point to review the situation. The relevant German weapons were a 37mm, two types of 50mm and the devastating 88s. This last was only really effective in a defensive situation since it was difficult to move quickly, and even when well emplaced, stuck up in the air like a tree. However it was not just their quality that made the German guns so effective, but the way they were used. During an attack they operated on the flanks of a tank force, moving forward alternately by stages so that hull-down tanks covered the movement of the guns and vice-versa. Such coordination, which was the hallmark of a German battle group, was one of the keys to Rommel's success. Many of these weapons were towed by sophisticated half-tracked tractors whose mobility in soft sand far exceeded that of the British four-wheel drive vehicles. Another innovation was the self-propelled anti-tank gun. The first type encountered in the desert was a 47mm weapon on a modified Panzer I chassis, but by the summer of 1942 large numbers of captured Russian 7.62mm weapons were starting to appear in both towed and self-propelled forms along with sleek, well armoured assault-guns based on the Panzer III.

The main British weapon was the 2-pounder, which was effective enough in its own way but impossible to use in the German fashion since it could not be fired accurately without first removing its wheels and unfolding a series of spindly legs. In response to the 88 the British had the 3.7 inch anti-aircraft gun which, in theory, was even more lethal against tanks. It, too, had a high silhouette and an unfortunate habit, when fired horizontally, of throwing a huge column of sand into the air which gave away its position. In any case the sights had to be modified for ground work and there was always a marked reluctance to jeopardise the air defence network in order to destroy tanks, which can probably be traced back to the effect of the Stukas in France. There was also the 25-pounder field gun which, in an emergency, made a fine anti-tank weapon, but only at the cost of disrupting the gunners' own fire-support programme. The British were even slower in developing self-propelled anti-tank guns on tracked chassis and none were completed in time to serve in the desert, although a curious half-measure was quite common. This was the portee, which was nothing more than a wheeled anti-tank gun mounted on the back of a lorry. Originally a French practice (hence the terminology) that dated back to the First World War, it developed in Britain for an altogether different reason.

In addition to the 2-pounder some anti-tank regiments in Britain were equipped with a dubious little 25mm weapon of French manufacture. It was so flimsy that towed behind a truck it invariably began to fall apart. As a remedy, throughout its brief career the gun was carried around in the back of a 15 cwt truck, although it had to be dismounted in order to be fired. At around the same time, in the desert 106 Battery, Royal Horse Artillery operated a portee system using 37mm Bofors anti-tank guns which could be fired from the rear of a 15 cwt truck. From this point the idea began to catch on, until in due course both 2-pounder and 6-pounder guns were used in this way in considerable numbers. Still, it was no way to fight tanks – the guns were a good deal higher, if more mobile in an emergency, and the crews were terribly vulnerable. The next obvious step was to build an armoured version but this was beyond the ability of local resources so the work was carried out in Britain. The result was Deacon, a modified AEC Matador gun-tractor fitted with an armoured cab and ammunition locker which mounted a 6-pounder behind a large shield on a turntable which gave a wide arc of fire. In this form it was not so much a portee, since the gun could not be dismounted, but a self-propelled mount of rather dubious mobility that was also extremely large. It did not appear in the desert until late 1942 and there is little positive evidence to show that it saw much active service.

The arrival of the Grant marked the first improvement, in terms of armament, that British tank men enjoyed during the war. In addition to the turret-mounted 37mm gun the tank carried a 75mm weapon in the side of the hull. It was not an ideal arrangement by any means, but much better than nothing. For one thing this gun could fire an effective high-explosive round in addition to normal anti-tank shot, which enabled it to deal with a wider variety of targets. It was also better armoured than Crusader without sacrificing much in the way of speed. All this was not before time. The Germans were also being equipped, albeit on a small scale, with a new version of the Panzer III mounting the longer 50mm gun. The advantage this conferred was mostly in terms of the range at which an action could be fought. It meant in effect that a German tank could open fire and start hitting its opponent before the British tank could get close enough to hit back. The Germans were also improving the defensive quality of their own tanks by welding extra layers of plate onto the front, and doing it at their base workshops in Libya without waiting for improved models to arrive from Germany. Even if the British could create the same facilities in Egypt it is doubtful if the tanks thus modified would have been able to bear the extra weight.

This was the real difference. In its basic form the Panzer III was a 1937 design, mounting a 37mm gun and with armour no thicker than 15mm on any part of it. By 1942 it had undergone two changes of armament and two substantial increases in armour thickness, first to 30mm and then to 50mm, plus the addition of extra 20mm plates bolted to the front. Over the same period its weight rose from 15.4 to 22.7 tons; a more powerful engine was installed so that its performance did not suffer, and the suspension had still coped adequately. No British tank of equivalent size or vintage could have done the same thing without collapsing. It is worth noting that the Germans chose only to uparmour the front of their tanks. This was

another lesson of the desert war and largely peculiar to it. Although it was perfectly possible to achieve surprise at a tactical level, by appearing out of the desert from an unexpected direction, the featureless landscape did not permit this to be continued once action had been joined. As soon as enemy tanks were sighted one would deploy to meet them head on.

Towards the end of May 1942 the tank situation on the Gazala Line was as follows: 32nd and 1st Army Tank Brigades were to the north although the former was without 4th RTR, which was in training for an amphibious landing as part of Auchinleck's new offensive. Seventh Armoured Division was to the south with its 22nd Armoured Brigade at a location called Knightsbridge, and the 2nd was some distance south east of that. First Armoured Division – represented at this stage only by 4th Armoured Brigade since 1st was back in Cairo re-equipping – was at the southern end of the line, covering the open flank. By this time both 3rd and 5th RTR of this Brigade had two squadrons of Grants and one of Stuarts, and it was these tanks that Rommel's 15th Panzer Division encountered on 27 May, the second day of the battle. For once the boot was on the other foot and the Germans found themselves under fire long before they were close enough to reply. Even so, despite heavy losses they retained the initiative and their mobility, and cut a swathe through the British rear areas with the intention of striking the coast road between Gazala and Tobruk. By the 29th it was clear that this could not be achieved and both 15th and 21st Panzer Divisions were recalled to join the surviving elements of the Italian Ariete Division in a defensive posture at Knightsbridge, with a strong British position in their rear. Rommel seemed to be trapped and now, if ever, was the opportunity to wipe him out. But the British dithered, and after two days of waiting for the hammer to fall the Germans turned about and destroyed the Sidi Muftah box – containing 150th Brigade along with elements of 42nd and 44th RTR – that were hemming them in from the west. A series of relatively minor actions (discounting Rommel's major attack on the Bir Hacheim box where the Free French gave him a very hard time) was followed by a substantial British assault on the German position, now known as the 'Cauldron', on 5 June. Starting with something like a two to one advantage in tanks the British failed to concentrate or coordinate, and persisted in throwing tanks against well-defended positions until the odds had changed in favour of the Germans.

The eventual fall of the Bir Hacheim position gave Rommel the freedom he needed to move north and cut off the British line of retreat from Gazala. Instead 15th and 21st Panzer Divisions became embroiled with British armour in the area east of Knightsbridge, but it was the British who came off worst. Hemmed in by the two German divisions, 2nd and 4th Armoured Brigades were rapidly whittled down to a fraction of their original strength before the survivors managed to break out of the trap. On the following day, 13 June, German attempts to eliminate the Knightsbridge box were frustrated by the British, and in particular the activities of the composite 7th/42th Royal Tank Regiment whose commander, Lieutenant-Colonel H R B Foote, was awarded the Victoria Cross for inspired leadership. Under cover of their tanks and a providential sandstorm the remaining British units managed to slip away, leaving Knightsbridge and most of their equipment to the Germans. It only remained to evacuate the northern part of the Gazala Line and this was achieved on the next day with some British losses: that they weren't greater was due as much to the exhausted state of the pursuing Germans as anything.

After one more heavy clash with 4th Armoured Brigade on 17 June Rommel turned his attention to Tobruk. The attack began before dawn on the 20th and ended twenty-four hours later with the surrender of the garrison, which included the remains of 4th and 7th RTR. What followed became known as the 'Gazala Gallop', but it was a race of tired jockeys on exhausted chargers, towards a finishing post that kept moving away. The first objective was the Egyptian frontier; then it became a line south from Mersah Matruh, and finally a narrow gap between the Qattara Depression and a small settlement near the coast called El Alamein, about 100 miles from Alexandria. It was an undignified scramble on both sides although the Germans at least knew where they were going. Indeed, by and large they got there first, and Rommel took a staggering risk with such a large British force still in his rear. Bleary-eyed drivers on both sides pushed their tanks eastwards with most of the crews asleep, slumped in bone-jarring discomfort in the turrets. Even Rommel's insistent drive could not overcome such weariness, and as his Panzers slowed down the British were regrouping. Rommel's aim, to confuse and panic the British commanders, worked well at an intermediate level but failed to shake Auchinleck who retained a firm grip on the situation. When the Germans paused for a day to allow the Italians to catch up they lost the one chance they might have had to break through.

It was not the end by any means; Rommel made two attempts to force the position early in July but his available tank strength was so low that he failed on each occasion. The British, too, were not content to rest and Auchinleck launched a series of counterattacks which, it was hoped, would destroy the overstretched Axis forces. None of these achieved their aims either, for a variety of reasons, and even the arrival of reinforcements did not help. Knowing Rommel's weakness the British attacked a different sector each time with varying results, but the worst by far occurred on 22 July. The newly arrived 23rd Armoured Brigade, comprising 40th, 46th and 50th RTR – all in Valentines – was directed to attack the enemy on and around Ruweisat Ridge in the wake of an overnight infantry assault. Inexperienced as they were the new regiments lost nothing, in terms of courage, to their battle-

hardened compatriots, but poor staff-preparation and inadequate communications combined to achieve their virtual destruction. They hit well-prepared German positions in an attack which, like some others, has been compared to the Charge of the Light Brigade at Balaclava. On this occasion the similarity was closer than most; about thirty tanks survived out of a total, for all three regiments, of over 150. The fighting continued on a diminishing scale until the end of July. By that time Auchinleck elected to remain on the defensive, improving the strength of his position and training up his troops for the next round. Rommel also needed time for once in order to build up his strength; audacity alone could not be relied upon. He needed tanks too.

Among the factors governing the success or otherwise of tanks in the desert, that of delivery might appear to be of little relevance. In fact it proved to be of considerable importance. Although the Germans received relatively few machines compared with the British, they had a decided advantage in what amounted to internal lines of communication. Their tanks could be moved by rail direct from Germany to port facilities in southern Italy with very little risk of interference. From here it was a relatively short sea-crossing to Tripoli, and although the Mediterranean was by no means an Italian lake the ships enjoyed good air cover from both shores and Sicily, which hampered British efforts to sink them. On the other hand British tanks had to cover the entire distance from their home ports to Egypt by sea, and even then not by the most direct route. Apart from the special and well-protected Tiger convoy already mentioned, most went the long way round. U-boat activity in the Western approaches obliged convoys to sweep well out into the Atlantic, almost to the American seaboard, before turning for the Cape and the long run up the east coast of Africa and through the Red Sea. Such a voyage could take the best part of five months, during which time the cargo received no particular attention except from the occasional pilferer, as mentioned earlier. A tank is hardly a delicate object but it still needs some care in transit and certainly would not improve in five months' exposure to sea air.

The original practice of simply lowering tanks into the hold and pulling on the handbrake, without making any attempt to strap them down, caused a lot of trouble. In rough weather a few would inevitably start to slide about and knock into their fellows, damaging suspension units or ripping off trackguards. It was not unknown for them to strike against the side of the ship, which not only damaged the tank but left a great bulge in the hull plating. Although they were battened down inside the holds, seawater and damp air infiltrated to cause even more trouble; the damp affected batteries and wiring while small castings, like the gear-lever housing on the Valentine, for instance, would corrode and crumble away so that they had to be replaced on arrival in Egypt. Equally dangerous was the practice of stacking other cargo on top of the tanks. If this worked loose in rough weather many small fittings such as periscopes, aerial bases and headlamps would be smashed, so that large quantities of spare parts also had to be shipped out and fitted to brand new tanks before they could be issued to regiments. It was an unnecessary and expensive vicious circle. Matters came to a head late in 1941 when a pair of Mark II Churchill tanks were shipped out for desert evaluation. They travelled as deck cargo and arrived in such a dreadful state that the matter was reported to the Prime Minister who, of course, thought he had a personal interest in them. A summary was made of the time required to prepare newly arrived tanks for active service and the worst cases recorded were two Matildas, each of which required over 400 man-hours. Indeed a specimen group of Crusaders, Matildas and Valentines, amounting to some 146 machines, needed a total of 10,000 skilled man-hours spent on them before they were fit for issue to operational units, and this did not include the extra time and cost involved in producing and shipping out the spare parts necessary to repair them.

Further, it was pointed out that the skilled men needed to undertake this work could only be found from workshops already heavily committed to the repair of battle-damaged or brokendown tanks from the desert.

As a result of Churchill's involvement standards soon began to improve. Of course it was easy enough for an overworked fitter in Egypt to forget what conditions were like in Britain, where docks were often singled out for bombing raids and stringent blackout regulations applied, but it was equally clear that tanks which deteriorated at sea were of no real use to anyone in the end, and could even cost lives. From now on tanks would be treated internally with rust preventatives and then completely sealed around all openings, while tools and other loose fittings were packaged separately in stout boxes and then wired firmly to the outside. Since they contained no fuel or water the tanks could not be driven in this state; they had to be towed from railway wagon or transporter to the crane, so the brake levers were operated by wires which led out through a wooden plug in the hull. Once aboard

89 Matilda tanks loading at a British port. Although this shipment was probably destined for Russia it serves to illustrate some of the measures taken to protect these vital machines at sea once the need for careful preparation was appreciated.

90 *A Tetrarch light tank in the Middle East. This is believed to be the only tank of this type sent out to the desert although a few more were used in the successful landings on Madagascar.*

ship they were tightly shackled down to stop them from moving about. On arrival in Egypt they were taken at once to a park where, as required, they could be opened, cleaned and restowed by unskilled labour, leaving only minor adjustments to be carried out by trained fitters. Such care would not make a bad tank any better, but at least it prevented good tanks from getting any worse.

The two Churchill tanks mentioned above arrived in Egypt in December 1941 so that their suitability for desert operations could be ascertained. This was handled by a branch of the Mechanisation Experimental Establishment which had been formed in the Middle East some time before the war. In fact they arrived in such poor condition that no useful tests could be made, but they were not the only types to be evaluated in this way. There is photographic evidence to show that other models, notably Covenanter and Tetrarch, also went out for the same purpose although neither type actually saw service in the desert.

At all times when armoured warfare is practised, the tank becomes a temporary home for its crew. In conditions of protracted warfare covering vast tracts of country this is even more pronounced, but in the desert where the opportunity to live off the country is nonexistent it assumes the greatest importance. As they became increasingly desert-wise the tank crews of Eighth Army went to such lengths to equip themselves with necessities and comforts that they earned a reputation for untidiness and individuality which became a matter of pride, perfectly summed up by the cartoonist Jon through the medium of his 'Two Types'. A typical Crusader of 7th Armoured

Division, as it roamed the desert, resembled a cross between a gipsy caravan and a tank, crewed by a party of tramps who had kitted themselves out at a jumble sale. Bedrolls and haversacks swung from the trackguards while a cooker and extra containers were strapped to the deck, and the interior was stuffed with greatcoats and anything else which might come in useful. An official report compared this tendency to Lewis Carroll's famous White Knight, who went to such lengths to equip himself with any and every thing that he might conceivably need on his travels that he was constantly falling off his horse. All tanks are provided with a series of internal and external lockers, designed to accommodate all the basic necessities, albeit heavily biased in favour of the tank rather than its crew. Ideally all their extra personal kit would be carried in lorries of the primary echelon with which the tanks could leaguer after a battle. Food could then be served up from mobile kitchens while NAAFI or YMCA trucks might also turn up with a few luxuries aboard. After a couple of rounds in the desert war it was realised that this ideal would often fail to materialise, and self-sufficiency became the order of the day. Food was carried in the tank and cooked on an ingenious stove; a tin filled with sand and soaked in petrol, which could be operational in an instant. A canvas awning would be rigged from the side of the tank beneath which the men would settle down in their bedrolls. It was very much the gipsy life with sand.

Actions like those which took place around Knightsbridge over a period of days, when the enemy was always close by, placed the crews under an even greater strain.

They might have to remain closed down throughout the daylight hours and often through the night as well. Supply lorries rarely got through and one thing that the men missed most was a hot drink. They might even have to sleep inside, curled up in utter discomfort, frozen at night and roasted by day. Reports from Vichy French sources that German tanks were air-conditioned caused an outcry in Britain and investigations began into how the system could be installed in British tanks. Further research revealed that no such requests had ever been initiated by British tank crews and that German tanks were not air-conditioned after all. Like their Allied counterparts, Axis tank crews just put up with it.

Communications also improved dramatically during the period under review. When the war began, those British tanks that were equipped with wireless either had the No 9 or No 11 sets. Both worked perfectly well but they were bulky, taking up a lot of room in a crowded turret, and heavy on current. The aerial was a thick, telescopic aluminium thing which was mounted on a folding bracket so that it could be made horizontal when not in use. This was an advantage in the flat desert landscape where a tall wireless aerial could give away the position of a tank which might be trying to hide in a fold of ground. Tanks equipped with the No 9 set also had a Tannoy internal communication system, while the No 11 had a separate circuit working through headphones. The drawback in both cases was that communication only worked one way, from commander to crew. Both were replaced in due course by the 19/24 set which was much more compact and less of a drain on the electrical system. The 19 was the 'A' set for long-distance communications while the 'B' set, the 24, was used for inter-squadron conversation over short range. Two aerials were required so the hinged bracket could not be used, but a new, slimmer rod aerial was used which was much less conspicuous. On the other hand the practice of flying identification pennants from the aerials, giving the correct signal of the day, had the opposite effect. A full crew intercommunication system was later added which allowed conversation in both directions, and proved very popular except when a crewman forgot to take off his headset before getting out. Although it suffered from teething troubles at first the new set soon proved to be extremely reliable, and popular with designers too, because it took up much less room.

To Churchill and the War Cabinet the situation in North Africa seemed inexplicable. Huge shipments of tanks and massive reinforcements of manpower had been poured into the theatre and apparently vanished into the desert. Despite a considerable superiority in men and material British and Commonwealth forces had often been outfought by one seemingly invincible German general in a region that was completely alien to him and his men. Determined to get to the root of the problem the Prime Minister flew out to Cairo early in August 1942 with his mind already made up that a change of command was

the only practical solution. Auchinleck was replaced by General Alexander while the Eighth Army was given to General Montgomery, following the death of the original appointee, General Gott, in another air crash. Lower down the scale Lieutenant-General Sir Oliver Leese took over 30 Corps and Lieutenant-General Sir Brian Horrocks 13 Corps. In order to let the new men settle in Auchinleck's proposed offensive was delayed for a month and this gave Rommel another chance – the last he was to get – to break through and capture Egypt and the Suez Canal for Hitler. Although the Germans had been reinforced this did not include any new tank formations, and the most useful addition to Rommel's Panzer force was about thirty of the latest Panzer IV mounting a long barrelled 75mm gun. The British called them Panzer IV Specials and they became the most formidable AFV on the desert scene. Had the tank fighting continued in the old way there is no doubt that these tanks, few as they were, would have had a considerable influence on the outcome, but it was not to be. Unlucky as he had been in the earlier battles there is every reason to believe that Auchinleck himself had the measure of Rommel, and he left the Eighth Army a legacy, in the form of the formidable Alamein position along with tactics that would now match the Germans at their own game.

Rommel's plan was to bypass the main Allied position on its southern flank and then sweep north, behind it, to strike at supply locations in the rear. This, he believed, would pose such a threat to Cairo and Alexandria that the British tanks would be obliged to come after him in the usual piecemeal way, inviting total destruction. The attack began on the night of 30 August, although the British had been expecting it for five days, but it immediately came unstuck when the minefield which covered the southern end of the British line was found to be much deeper than expected. This, coupled with delays to his resupply column, almost persuaded Rommel to call the attack off but instead he modified it, swinging north earlier than planned to hit the British on Alam Halfa Ridge which ran parallel and to the south of Ruweisat Ridge. In the first stage the attackers were also harassed by the Stuarts and Crusaders of 7th Armoured Division, posted to cover the open flank, and by the RAF which began to hit consistently and hard throughout the day. Thus delayed, it was late afternoon before the Germans were in sight from Alam Halfa and it was noticed that they were acting cautiously, expecting no doubt to be assailed at any moment by the usual death-or-glory British tank charge that they were ready to deal with. The tanks were there all right, but they were not moving. Having learned their lesson the hard way, and hearing it drummed into them by Auchinleck, they would not be tempted out again. Concealed in hollows at the foot of the ridge were the anti-tank guns, the 6-pounders; but there was nowhere here to hide a Grant. With their high superstructure and offset main armament these tanks needed better cover, so they were ensconsed in the foothills, often in specially prepared positions.

The tanks belonged to the 4th County of London Yeomanry (CLY), 1st RTR, 5th RTR and the Greys, which now comprised 22nd Armoured Brigade, commanded by Colonel 'Pip' Roberts. Each regiment mustered two squadrons of Grants to one of Crusaders or Stuarts. It will be noted that for this battle 22nd Armoured Brigade fielded four regiments and the first three were emplaced in the hills. The Greys, away to the left, had the newest and hopefully the most reliable Grants, so they were detailed as the mobile reserve. The Germans ran straight on to the British positions and came off worst in the short fight that ensued before darkness fell. Next morning they began, cautiously again, to feel their way eastwards and closed with 4th CLY who lost a number of tanks to the new Panzer IVs. Then the Greys came up in support and it was clear that overall it was the Germans who were losing most tanks. Fighting continued throughout the afternoon but on the following day, 1 September, 23rd Armoured Brigade came down to cover the right flank while 8th Armoured Brigade moved in from the east. Short of fuel and under continual air attack Rommel knew he could do no more, and ordered a withdrawal, to commence on the 2nd. Montgomery had reached the same conclusion and planned to trap the Germans by closing the gap they had made in the minefield. But he was too cautious, fearful of letting his tanks advance and fall into one of Rommel's famous traps, so he employed three infantry brigades, supported only by two squadrons of 46th and 50th RTR, many of which accidentally ran into the minefield themselves and were lost. Thus the Germans, over the next three days, successfully disengaged from what a British report called 'The Battle of the Bloody Nose'.

Alam Halfa was a new experience for both sides. The heady days of dashing all over the desert – which had suited the British when they were fighting the Italians, and the Germans when they took on the British – were gone. The Germans would continue to use their armour with intelligence, verve and courage, but they were desperately short of equipment. The British had overwhelming strength on their side but they could see where they had gone wrong and used tanks with a good deal more skill, without losing a healthy respect for every element of the Afrika Korps. On the British side too, more new equipment was entering the fray and the new divisional establishment, already adopted at home, was starting to appear in the desert. Foremost among the new tanks was the Sherman with its 75mm main armament in the turret. Over 200 were shipped to the Middle East by October direct from the USA, along with more Grants and their American equivalent, the Lee. Improved models of the Valentine would be appearing too, with a larger three-man turret, although for the present still mounting the 2-pounder gun. Matildas had been converted into Scorpions, crude minesweeping tanks, while another weapon new to the British Army in this war was about to enter service – the self-propelled gun.

The early development of specialised armour is covered in the next chapter, but strictly speaking, self-propelled artillery falls outside the scope of this book and can be mentioned only briefly. As already noted it was a field in which the Germans had established a commanding lead,

91 *The crew of this M3 Grant look down upon a burning Panzer I as they pass by.*

and British attempts to catch up were never very impressive. The first was an emergency measure initiated in Britain at a time when it seemed as if the 2-pounder was never going to be replaced and the Germans were still expected to cross the Channel. An obsolete type of anti-aircraft gun (although it was still in service), the 3-inch 20 cwt, was mounted within a rectangular superstructure on the Churchill hull. It was heavy, slow and box-like, but if put to the test it would have proved a powerful and effective tank destroyer. As it was nobody could ever decide who should operate them, the Gunners or the RAC, they were never issued to service and production ceased after fifty had been built. This smacks of the kind of pedantic foolishness that often bedevilled British service relationships to the detriment of the common good. The Valentine Bishop, on the other hand, a much less impressive design, was unarguably Royal Artillery equipment since it mounted the 25-pounder. The design stemmed from a request first expressed in the desert where towed guns, behind wheeled tractors, were always getting bogged down in the sand. Facilities were not available to produce anything suitable in Egypt so the problem was passed back to the United Kingdom. The result was a Valentine hull, mounting the 25-pounder over the turret ring and enclosed within a tall armoured box. It was not so much a design as an improvisation, and a bad one at that, since the superstructure was cramped and so shaped that it imposed severe limitations on the gun's ability to elevate, thus effectively limiting its range. There was also insufficient room inside the armoured housing for the crew to serve the gun so a pair of doors opened out on to the engine deck where the loader had to squat in order to attend the breech. The extra weight, coupled with the fact that each gun had to tow an ammunition limber to ensure a reasonable supply, slowed the Bishop down so that it could not even keep pace with the tanks it was meant to support, and in this as in other respects it fell a long way short of expectations. The very opposite was true of an American design, the M7, which British soldiers called the Priest. It gave the edge to mobility over the need for protection since the gun crew worked in an open-top compartment, and it was roomier as it was based on a bigger vehicle. The entire chassis from track and suspension to engine and transmission were pure Lee, or Grant. The complete front superstructure and turret were replaced by a lightly armoured casemate with a 105mm howitzer mounted at the front. To its right was a circular machine-gun mounting which from its pulpit-like appearance gave the vehicle its name. Priests were in service with the Royal Artillery by October 1942 so they were ready to take part in the next great battle.

The second battle of El Alamein, as it came to be called, began on the night of 23 October 1942. On the Allied side over 1000 tanks were available with another 200 due to arrive at any time, while at least that number again were in Egypt, either undergoing repair, in preparation, or attached to schools and special units. The Germans had about 280, including tanks under repair, and the Italians had a similar number, but this reckons without self-propelled guns or the all-powerful towed 88s. The Germans were also without Rommel, their inspiration, who had gone home for medical treatment leaving General Stumme in command. Rommel flew back as soon as the attack was reported but in the meantime Stumme collapsed and died of a heart attack. The Afrika Korps could function without its leaders for a while, but it could not manage without supplies, especially fuel. This was the real problem; the Royal Navy and RAF were beginning to dominate the western Mediterranean to such an extent that few Axis ships and no tankers were getting through with replenishments. While he was conserving fuel Rommel could not afford to be as flexible as he wished, nor to make any mistakes, which was an intolerable position to be in.

Any attempt to catalogue the armoured units available to General Montgomery would require an inordinate amount of space, and in any case the information is available elsewhere, but there were seven armoured brigades and a similar number of armoured car regiments; three troops of minesweeping tanks and two regiments of dummy tanks. All were either grouped in three armoured divisions, 1st, 7th and 10th, or allotted directly under Corps and Army control. Montgomery has gained a reputation as a man who husbanded his resources and employed caution, even from a position of overwhelming strength. In the same situation it is likely that Rommel would have employed most of his armour in one formidable phalanx, but the British commander preferred to spread his out, giving himself the freedom and flexibility to switch the main thrust of his attack as the situation demanded. This would serve to throw the enemy off balance and, hopefully, tie up some of his strength in covering areas that might be threatened. Montgomery's intention was to attack in such a way that he drew enemy tank units onto his own when they were in favourable positions, and to wipe them out bit by bit. It had been tried before, usually with only limited success, but now the Allies could afford to lose two tanks to the Germans' one and still end up with superior numbers.

For its initial success El Alamein required that the attackers would drive corridors through large Axis minefields on the first night through which the armour could pour to be in strong defensive positions by dawn, which Rommel would be invited to attack. In fact it took three days and the loss of large numbers of tanks before the British had these minefields behind them, and even then there was no sign of a breakthrough. Indeed by the night of 26 October things looked so bad that the offensive was halted and new plans drawn up which came into effect two days later. More well-defended minefields were encountered and once again the attack ground to a halt. It then took five more days to organise another new attack. This too got off to a bad start, but led to a fullscale tank

92 *Sherman II (M4A1) tanks in British service form up to pursue the retreating Axis forces after Alamein.*

battle in the area of Tel el Aqqaqir which, although costly to the British, decimated Rommel's tank strength. Now he had no option but to withdraw, and would have done so had he not received – for the first time in the entire campaign – peremptory orders from Hitler to stay where he was. Unused to such direct personal interest (which was to increase and dismay many a German general before the war was over) he saw no course but to obey. The result was that on the night of 2 November 1942 the final breakthrough was achieved by 5th Indian Brigade supported by 50th RTR, and Rommel simply had to retreat. Even so it was in no sense a rout. Although they were losing nearly as many tanks through shortage of fuel as from fighting the Germans and Italians obliged the Allies to fight all the way. Montgomery had studied Rommel and knew his wily ways. Many times before the Desert Fox had seemed to be beaten, only to turn and savage his tormentors while regaining the initiative – so even with victory in his grasp Montgomery was not going to fall for that.

The British did not start to cross the Libyan frontier until 11 November and by that time mud, caused by the first heavy rain of the season, began to slow them down. It took the best part of a month before they found themselves forming up before the next major German defensive position. This was at Agheila, the highwater mark of the British advance in 1940. Here Rommel elected to make a stand. At one stage during the retreat the Afrika Korps had been reduced to a total of ten serviceable tanks, but now it was joined by a new Italian armoured division, Centauro. Yet behind Rommel, in Tunisia, the Allies had landed in strength, and unless he could hold Tripoli his chances of getting any part of his army safely back to Europe would be gone. It was the middle of December before the Eighth Army mounted its attack on the Agheila position, and almost at once the German and Italian forces withdrew. For another six weeks they maintained a controlled retreat ahead of a cautious Allied advance, but the result was never in doubt. British tanks rolled, virtually unopposed, onto the streets of Tripoli early in the morning of 23 January 1943.

To the British tank men the new star of the show was the Sherman. It added to the performance and reliability of the Grant the advantage of a useful gun in a fully

93 *A diesel powered Sherman III (M4A2) tank is unloaded by a floating crane off Alexandria while ships from the convoy lie at anchor beyond.*

rotating turret. Crews also appreciated the thicker armour which at least gave them a fair chance against the latest version of the Panzer IV. They had few complimentary things to say about the Crusader III, the version mounting a 6-pounder gun in the two-man turret, probably because by this time the tank had such a dreadful reputation for unreliability that no improvement in firepower could be seen as very much compensation. They were much more impressed with the Churchill, which had only appeared in small numbers on a trial basis in time for Alamein. Six of the Mark III version, mounting the 6-pounder gun in a welded turret, formed Kingforce, under Major Norris King MC of the Royal Gloucestershire Hussars. They arrived shortly before the battle and were attached to HQ, 1st Armoured Division, for the attack. One was lost but the remainder took part in the big tank action at Tel el Aqqaqir. They acquitted themselves well. Their ability to absorb punishment was little short of astounding by the standards of the time and fears about their cooling systems – which had been specifically designed for European climes – proved to be unfounded. These were the only Churchills to operate with the Eighth Army in North Africa and they did not take part in the subsequent pursuit across Libya, so the test could only be seen as a limited one.

One of the recurring problems of armoured warfare is the distance a tank can travel on one fill of fuel. In the desert, where the ability to move over long distances with very little preparation is of paramount importance, it became a key factor. Tank design is all about the economic use of space, and since fuel tanks must be well protected it follows that capacity is always limited. As an example, the diesel-engined Valentine II had a range of 110 miles on its two internal fuel tanks; if an external tank was fitted it would travel another ninety miles. This proved to be the most successful answer, although it did not solve the problem entirely. The auxiliary fuel-tank was an un-armoured drum mounted, in the case of the Valentine, on the trackguard. Because it was not bulletproof it was obviously not a good idea to carry it into battle (in a petrol-engined tank it could prove disastrous) so the extra fuel was only used to supply the tank during an approach march. Once shells started flying about it was jettisoned by a quick release mechanism from the driver's position, and the main fuel tanks came into action: they, of course should still have been nearly full.

Although the system worked quite well, and was pro-bably a lot better than the German habit of driving about with a lot of full Jerricans stowed on the hull or turret-roof, it did not dissuade people from trying to come up with something better. One result was the Rotatrailer which, in practice, turned out to be a lot worse. Various trailers had been tested in Britain before the Rotatrailer was devised but it was considered the best, and entered production in the hands of the Tecalemit Company. Basi-cally it was an armoured box, complete with lid, running on two hollow wheels fitted with solid rubber tyres. It was attached to a quick-release hook on the back of the tank by a solid drawbar. Although there were variations a typical Rotatrailer was divided into two compartments. The front section was used to stow extra ammunition while the rear part contained a small hand-operated pump and hose. The hollow wheels were then filled with fuel which could be pumped into the tank when required. They appear to have been tested very thoroughly in Britain, and the results must have been fairly satisfactory or they would not have been shipped out to the desert. Here it was a different story. The wheels would leak at the hubs, and despite copious applications of grease the combined effects of heat, gritty sand and jolting over rocky ground destroyed the seals until precious fuel was seeping out into the sand. But there was worse to come: Rotatrailers were unsprung, and on long desert treks, whenever hard, rocky ground was encountered, they would start to leap about until the action got too violent and the trailer bounced high enough to land upsidedown. Without help the crew would be unable to right it, and in any case the towbar was often so badly twisted that it could not be used. There was no more heartfelt plea than that contained

94 *Churchill III tanks of Kingforce before Alamein. The canvas 'dodger' slung across the front was designed to prevent sand from blowing up into the driver's face.*

in the signal sent back to the authorities in Britain urging them to stop sending the blessed things out. But still they came, uselessly taking up space in ships which could be better employed to carry tanks. Men who still considered themselves desperate for more tanks could only gaze in frustration at the vehicle parks with their ever-growing stocks of Rotatrailers that nobody would use.

95 One of the much maligned Rotatrailers showing the rear compartment open and the pump linked up to the fuel cap on the right side wheel.

8 The return of specialised armour

96   *The crew of this Cruiser Mark IVA survey the damage caused by a mine. Notice how the track has broken and, in doing so, torn most of the tin-work off the side.*

The tank had been devised in the first place to fulfil a distinct and very limited function on the battlefield, but even before the end of the First World War it was realised that armoured vehicles were capable of undertaking various tasks. By 1919 tanks had been developed which could clear mines, lay bridges and place demolition charges, while others had been adapted to swim. The soldier began to appreciate that machines could not only provide the power to do these things, and do them quickly, they could also protect the men who operated them at the same time.

Interest in this aspect of armoured warfare tended to lapse between the wars and was not revived with any degree of enthusiasm until 1937. Once war broke out again the need for special-purpose tanks was even more obvious and the process of invention accelerated, but it was not pursued on an organised basis. Apart from the Experimental Bridging Establishment, whose function was clearly defined, no specific body was appointed to oversee experiments, and no programme was devised to ensure that development proceeded in a properly coordinated fashion. Matters improved later in the war but for the first three years it was simply a case of shoestring developments appearing as and when the need for them was appreciated. Yet once the concept caught on it was pursued with great enthusiasm by the British Army. Other nations dabbled, and used such equipment in a small way, but in Britain specialised armour, as this business of modifying tanks was called, was considered second only in importance to the fighting tanks themselves.

The mine has always been seen as one of the most insidious enemies of the tank. It was not necessarily productive of high casualties since it mostly attacked tracks and suspension, but the tank was effectively disabled until it could be recovered, if it was not shot to pieces in the meantime. Lighter vehicles suffered much more; a carrier or scout car could be turned right over by the blast and the crew killed, while a Jeep or truck could be blown to pieces. Mine clearance was a Royal Engineers responsibility and men were trained to detect and lift them by hand, which was a very costly and time-consuming business. Furthermore it was patently ridiculous to hold tanks in check while unprotected soldiers swept a path for them, so in 1937 the General Staff addressed the problem of making tanks do their own minesweeping. Investigations were carried out into the various properties of mines, and two methods of dealing with them were proposed.

The first was intended for use in zones where fixed defences had to be assaulted and deep, permanent minefields could be expected. Such objectives were the original province of infantry tanks so initial experiments were carried out on the little A11. The object was not to explode the offending mines but to lift and turn them aside from the path of the tank to where they could be rendered safe later. Some sort of plough device seemed to be the obvious answer, so two agricultural engineering firms, John Fowlers of Leeds and Harry Ferguson's tractor company, were asked to develop prototypes. Ferguson appears to have dropped out of the scheme at an early stage but Fowlers filed a patent for a device which, following tests on an artillery tractor, was adopted as the Coulter Plough. It consisted of a frame, attached to the tank, which projected in front and carried a series of long tines which would turn up the soil, and the mines with it. There were drawbacks of course; while it was pushing the plough the tank could not proceed at more than 3 mph and there was always a chance that a mine would roll back and fall under the tracks. Hard, frozen ground could defeat the plough, as could tree roots and inequalities in the ground level but, in general, the trial set fitted to A11E1 performed surprisingly well. Although some of the weight of the apparatus was borne by built-in rollers it was obvious that for normal running the device would have to be raised clear of the ground, so a power-operated winch was fitted to the back of the tank, driven off the final drive, which held the frame at an angle, pivoting on the sides of the tank. It made the vehicle rather nose heavy and prevented

97 *The Coulter Plough device fitted to an Infantry Tank Mark I. The chain and pulley system at the rear is part of the power operated lifting gear.*

98 *Anti-Mine Roller Attachment Mark IC fitted to a Covenanter. A test mine has just been exploded on the far side and probably destroyed one of the rollers in the process. By looking closely one can just see part of the canvas cover which lies over the device.*

99 *This Valentine has been fitted with a variety of mine detonating rollers made locally in the Middle East. Even if they did protect the tank they must have seriously impaired its mobility.*

it from using its gun, but it was all there was, so production went ahead.

A number of modifications were specified to suit the ploughs to production tanks and Fowlers also devised a wire-cutting attachment that fitted to the front. It had been intended to provide a Coulter Plough for each Infantry Tank Mark I but the first sixty were already in production when the design was finalised so the special fittings were only built onto the second batch. Deliveries began to the three RTC Battalions, 4th, 7th and 8th (the only units to employ the A11) from January 1940, but there is no evidence that they were ever used with the tanks. While the Germans were doing all the advancing they had no need of minefields. Consequently when most of the tanks were lost in France the balance of the order was cancelled. Plans were drawn up to fit a similar device to the A12 Matilda but they had not progressed far when it was discovered that in order to operate a mechanical lifting apparatus, an extra gearbox would have to be mounted at the back of the tank, and this complication killed the project.

The second type of minesweeping device was intended for use on cruiser tanks. Since these were designed for long-range operations, rather than head-on attacks against fixed positions, the concept was somewhat different. Under these circumstances a tank is likely to encounter mines anywhere on the battlefield without prior warning, so it was considered essential that the equipment chosen should be readily available for use without inhibiting the tank's progress to any great extent. For this reason rollers were chosen instead of a plough, but these would not excavate a mine, they would explode it. The equipment was tested on the prototype Cruiser Mark I but it took a lot longer to develop and did not enter service until 1942. Known as the Anti-Mine Roller Attachment it consisted of a frame fitted to arms which pivoted on each side of the tank, with four heavy rollers suspended from it, two in front of each track. In the original scheme the entire assembly would be raised clear of the ground by hydraulic action and held there until such time as it was needed. Once the presence of mines was suspected it would be lowered and pushed in front of the tank. When a roller ran over a mine detonation occurred and invariably the roller was destroyed. Unless the mined area was too extensive the tank would hope to get through before all its rollers were destroyed and the vehicle itself began to suffer. In order to assess the effect of mines going off in close proximity to a tank the prototype was tested on one occasion with a crew of rabbits. One assumes that the tank was being towed or pushed at this time since the rabbits could hardly drive it, and presumably they survived. Once it got clear of the mines the tank could jettison the damaged frame and proceed about its business.

Mines vary in many ways and the pressure required to detonate them differs. Consequently the roller attachment had to be adjustable for weight. The original pattern,

again developed by Fowlers, used an open, spoked type of roller, but it was later replaced by a hollow drum type which could be filled with sand, rubble or water to increase the pressure as required. Another refinement was a small canvas curtain which could be unrolled over the frame to prevent sand or dust being thrown up to obscure the driver's periscopes. By the time they were introduced the requirement for a hydraulic lift had been dropped and the device was normally carried in a lorry until it was needed. It could easily be fitted by four men. Five versions were produced, Marks I A – D which fitted Matilda, Valentine, Covenanter and Crusader (in that order) and Mark IIE which was designed for Churchill. This last version had four twin sets of rollers, two on each side, followed by two singles which covered the narrow gap between each twin set. They were issued to some tank units in the desert but if one relies upon photographic evidence, which is all that is available, the impression is that they were rarely used.

Another type of roller, developed locally in the Middle East, consisted of a drum of concrete with inset spikes. It first appeared on specially modified Canadian Military Pattern lorries, Fords or Chevrolets. When the vehicle approached a minefield the driver would transfer from the cab to a protected position inside an armoured cylinder which stood in the truck bed. Similar equipment was tested on Valentine tanks and AEC Armoured Cars. In Britain a Valentine was modified by the Hungarian inventor Nicholas Straussler. It was equipped with a front-mounted frame which carried four long leafsprings and eight counterbalanced prongs which literally raked the ground. The effect of an exploding mine would be dissipated partly by the springs and by the swinging action of the prong, which would then be forced back into place by the weighted arm, but it was never adopted for service. Others were equally unsuccessful. A French device consisting of a series of steel discs pushed ahead of a tank was

100 Nicholas Straussler's complex but ingenious mine clearing rake mounted on a Valentine. In the far corner of the workshop can be seen a Universal Carrier with the inventor's collapsible floats fitted.

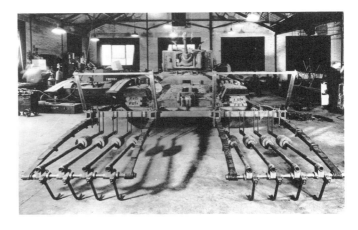

rejected after trials when it was found that the propelling vehicle was unable to steer. Another type, invented in Britain, used expendable weights held, like bullets, in a magazine. If a weight was destroyed the next one simply slipped down to take its place, but this did not work either. It was also discovered that mines could be destroyed by sympathetic detonation if an explosive charge was set off near them, and attempts were made to apply this to tanks. It resulted in the development of Snake, an explosive-filled tube that was pushed ahead of a tank and set off to clear a path through the minefield. It was first used in the latter stages of the desert campaign, attached to Valentine tanks.

Ultimately the most effective mine-clearing device was found to be the flail. The idea had been investigated before the war but was not developed at that time and had probably been forgotten. In the summer of 1941 a South African, Major A S J du Toit, came up with a similar idea. A test rig was built on a lorry and demonstrated in Pretoria, where a short film was made. When this was seen by General Auchinleck he had du Toit sent to Britain where, it was hoped, his idea could be perfected. One of those who had seen it in Pretoria was Captain Norman Berry RAOC, and he believed that the best place to experiment was the desert, where nobody would see what was going on, but he was overruled. In the following May he tried to discover what progress had been made in Britain by asking any visiting experimental officer what he knew about it. He could learn nothing; du Toit and what he called his threshing machine seemed to have disappeared. Determined to do something on his own initiative Berry organised a special workshop unit and set to work. The first experiment was based on a Ford lorry. The stripped chassis of a second vehicle was slung, back to front, from the original lorry and its engine used to drive a pair of flail drums mounted in place of the rear wheels. Rommel's summer offensive then began and might have captured the experimental vehicle had it not been driven quickly back to El Alamein. While the army sorted itself out nothing more could be done. When work did start again it was on a more official footing and the prototype was placed in the hands of 21st Field Company, South African Construction Company, who fitted a modified system to a Matilda tank. It proved so successful when compared with the roller type minesweeper that an immediate order was placed for twenty-four. It was a tall order, since they were required within a month, made all the more difficult when the plan to use Lincoln Zephyr V12 engines had to be abandoned since they could not be made available in time. In their place Ford V8 engines were used which were not really powerful enough. This engine, which drove the flail rotor, was located in a housing on the right side of the tank. From here the driveshaft passed to the flail drum which projected ahead of the tank on a pair of lattice girder arms. As the drum rotated a selection of cable and chain flails beat the ground and exploded any mines they

struck, clearing a path one tank wide across the minefield. Like all new inventions the Matilda Scorpion, as this device was called, was hardly ideal. For one thing it was necessary to station a man inside the motor compartment on the side of the tank where he could control the flail engine and restart it when it stalled. It was hot, noisy, cramped and uncomfortable in every way but a Sapper Docherty, who worked in one at El Alamein, expressed the opinion it was preferable to lifting mines by hand, especially under mortar fire.

Construction of the first models was undertaken by No 7 Base Workshop in Alexandria, and the Scorpions were issued to 42nd and 44th RTR, formed as 1st Army Tank Brigade under HQ Eighth Army control, and parceled out to 30 Corps. There were too few of them to cover the front effectively, and in order to produce a wide enough lane for other tanks to use it was necessary to flail a path across to the enemy side of a minefield, turn round, and flail a parallel one back to the home side. It was dangerous work – one might always miss a mine, and at a maximum flailing speed of 0.5 mph the tank was a sitting duck for enemy weapons. Furthermore, the flail engine was liable to overheat, especially if any barbed wire wrapped itself around the drum, and once stalled it was usually impossible to start again. In fact there are few recorded instances of Scorpions achieving the double run at El Alamein; one that nearly did was halfway back when it met some Crusader tanks going the other way. These elbowed it off the beaten path and on to three mines which had been lifted and laid alongside the gap. Both tracks were blown off.

Although Berry, in the Middle East, had heard nothing about it du Toit's trip to Britain was not wasted. Backed up by a telegram from Auchinleck which praised the potential of his 'anti-tank mine springing device' he was sent to work with engineers at AEC Ltd in Southall, in cooperation with the Department of Tank Design. Auchinleck rather overstated the case when he said that it could clear minefields and wire obstacles as well as destroying pillboxes – although how he thought it could do this is not clear – but it was obvious that the idea had some merit. The prototype produced by AEC was also based on a Matilda and, not surprisingly, looked very similar to the Middle East version. It was given the codename Baron, perhaps because gentlemen of that stamp once used to carry chain flails to war. Compared with Scorpion there was one refinement; a hydraulically operated pump, working off the tank's turret-control system, which raised and lowered the flail boom. This served two purposes. The operator, who on this version worked from within the tank itself, could adjust the height of the rotor to suit the ground he hoped to clear, and the entire jib could be elevated for normal road travel well clear of the ground.

The first model, Baron I, employed a six-cylinder Chrysler engine with its own radiator to work the flail, but it was seriously underpowered and the equipment was rebuilt. It now emerged as Baron II with a more powerful

Bedford engine which drew its coolant from the tank's own system. Unlike Baron I, which employed chains and sprockets to drive the rotor, Baron II used shaft drive, incorporating universal joints. It was also fitted with a wirecutting device on the drum which brought it closer to General Auchinleck's ideal, but it still could not break up pillboxes. However, these cutters had one other function. Since the jib height was adjustable it could be lowered to the ground to dig away at earth banks, 'somewhat akin to the scratching of a dog' according to a REME report, and in a trial a 12-foot gap was opened in a sandy bank, 3-feet high and 9-feet deep, in six minutes. In the process the tank was showered with soil until the driver was unable to see what he was doing, and experiments with wipers or jets of exhaust gas blown on to the periscopes failed to keep them clean. In any event, this model also suffered from overheating and had to be abandoned.

Like the Scorpions these two Barons carried a fully armed turret although it was unable to fire over a 30° arc at the front for fear of damaging the flail gear, so it was not very much use. On the third model, Baron III, the turret was dispensed with, although when it appeared towards the end of 1942 it was still based on the Matilda. The turret was replaced by an armoured operator's cab, and two Bedford engines in protected housings were fitted on the sides of the hull. Now, at last, there was sufficient power, although in order to work effectively the tank was only able to move at 0.25 mph while flailing. Up to this time all flails worked the same way, with the drum rotating in the direction of travel. Engineers wondered if the job would be done better if the drum turned against the direction of travel, but this initiated detonation a lot closer to the tank and was rejected as unsafe. The Baron III was much too wide to cross a Bailey bridge or pass through the bow doors of a landing craft, but at least it worked, so with one small modification it was accepted for service. This involved replacing the tank's hydraulic traversing pump by a separate one driven off the engine and in this

form, as Baron IIIA, sixty were ordered from Curran Brothers of Cardiff.

In December 1942 the War Office was apparently surprised to receive a report on the development of Scorpions in the Middle East. The impression given is that until that time they had no idea any such thing was going on, let alone that it had been used in action – which is surprising because it had even been reported, rather vaguely, in the *Daily Express*. The only immediate reaction seems to have been a suggestion that Scorpions should be renamed 'Baron, Middle East Pattern', which was never done.

Tanks that could carry and launch their own bridges across impassable obstacles under fire would clearly be extremely useful, and some working prototypes had been developed at the end of the First World War. An Experimental Bridging Establishment (EBE) had been created on the banks of the River Stour at Christchurch and this survived the inter-war cuts because it also dealt in other aspects of military bridging. The famous Bailey Bridge was developed there. A few tank-related experiments had also been carried out but it was not until 1936 that they really got going. In that year General Martel had initiated the design of a self-propelled bridgelayer on a Dragon chassis which worked after a fashion but was so long

102 *A Matilda Baron Mark IIIA flailing during trials in Britain. The shaft drive from the engine housing is clearly seen on the left.*

101 *Matilda Scorpion flails moving up to clear mines at El Alamein. The flail operator, crouching behind the turret, will climb inside the motor box when they go into action.*

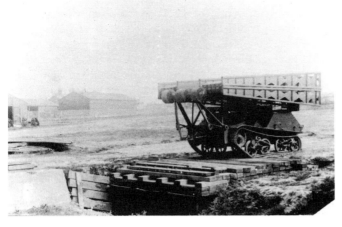

103–107   A sequence of pictures showing the launching procedure of a scissors bridge. This is the prototype design based on the hull of a Light Mark V tank.

that it proved difficult to handle in confined spaces. A refinement was then worked out by Captain S G Galpin RE in which the bridge was stowed folded on top of a turretless tank and opened out like a pair of scissors as it was launched. Galpin worked on the basis of a hydraulic launching arrangement and even started to make a small model, based on a cardboard shoebox, to demonstrate his idea. Pressure of other work forced him to abandon the project but in 1939 it was resurrected by the staff at EBE. One of them took the model home to complete it but found it impossible to recreate the hydraulic gear in miniature, so simply in order to illustrate the principle he substituted a long, threaded rod which turned in a fixed nut to achieve the same effect. When the fullsize design was being worked out in the drawing office at Christchurch it was soon realised that this system actually had an advantage over hydraulics, in that the turning screw gave very fine control along with the ability to hold the bridge firmly in any position between closed and fully open. Experiments went ahead on this basis and a redundant tank served as a prototype. The vehicle in question was the light tank L3E1, one of the pilot models of the Light Mark V, which was stripped of its turret and fitted with a power take-off to operate the screw gear. This was basically an extra driveshaft running off the tank's gearbox, which passed upwards into an auxiliary gearbox through which the threaded rod passed. Rotating gears within this box caused the rod to turn, and as it worked its way through it activated a series of levers which launched the bridge or recovered it, as required.

The bridge consisted of two pairs of ramps, hinged in the middle, which opened out to form a bridge 26-feet long, which was capable of carrying a 5-ton light tank – in other words anything up to the size of a Light Mark VI. In place, on top of the turretless tank, the bridge remained folded, with the hinge to the rear. As the thread unwound it pushed the nose of the bridge forwards by

pivoting the cradle on which it lay, until rollers on the latter were touching the ground and the bridge, still in its folded state, was vertical. Further action of the thread caused the bridge to complete its somersault, but as it did so, a series of cables and pulleys opened it out so that the upper half began to reach to the opposite side of the gap. The action was complete when the fully opened bridge came to rest across the gap, at which point the tank could disengage and move away. Obviously the whole operation could be gone through in reverse to pick up the bridge again but the point was that the entire operation could be carried out by a crew who were safely shut up inside the tank; nobody had to get out and place themselves at risk.

So successful was it that the War Office, instead of ordering immediate production, demanded that the prototype be sent at once to the Middle East where Wavell's first assault on Bardia was due to begin. The bridgelayer would probably have been used to span the anti-tank ditch which protected the place. There is no record of it ever arriving in North Africa, let alone being used, and that was the last Christchurch ever heard of it.

There is some suggestion that a second prototype was built, but by this time the light tank had no serious military future and it was never developed. On the other hand there was no reason why the same principle could not be adapted to larger machines, and it was.

While work on the Light Scissors Bridge Tank went ahead other ideas were tried. One involved an armoured version of the standard Caterpillar D8 crawler tractor. This towed a 30-foot box-girder bridge behind it on a small pair of wheels until it arrived at the obstacle to be crossed. The bridge was then winched up on an 'A' frame until it was clear of the ground and the whole thing hung out behind the tractor. The driver then swung the whole ensemble through 180° until the bridge was suspended over the gap, ready for dropping. MB Wild and Co, makers of Coles Cranes, also put forward an idea in 1938 for a cable-launched bridge in two halves, stowed one above the other on the vehicle. It was a complicated

system which never achieved one successful launch and recovery during trials, and neither type ever progressed beyond the prototype stage.

The next development in the scissors bridge story began when the EBE was asked to adapt it for the A10 cruiser tank. In fact it required a complete redesign to suit the bigger vehicle and the opportunity was taken to alter the angle at which the bridge was laid, in case the far bank turned out to be higher than that on the launching side. The bridge itself was longer, capable of spanning a 30-foot gap, and of carrying a 24-ton tank. Thus the A10 was quite suitable as a bridgelayer for handling any tank then in service except the A12 Matilda and the new Churchill. Yet for some reason, rather than make good use of obsolete tanks, the War Office decided that in future bridgelayers should be built on the chassis of current service models. Consequently the Covenanter was the next choice, so the team at Christchurch set out to redesign the launching gear to suit, although the same bridge was used. This model passed from the prototype stage and actually entered production before it too was passed over in favour of the Valentine, and the equipment had to be redesigned yet again. This gave the definitive model which remained in service until the end of the war, but even the Covenanter made a brief comeback – a few were supplied to the Australians, who used them operationally in the Far East.

The contractor for scissors-bridge conversions was the Southern Railway, at their Eastleigh Works near Southampton, and it is interesting to note that the redundant turrets from these Valentine tanks were used to complete the first batch of AEC Mark I armoured cars. It is also worth commenting that, obsolete or not, the A10 bridgelayer was the only version that retained any sort of offensive armament in the form of the hull-mounted Besa machine-gun.

The devices so far described could fairly claim to be basic military functions translated into the context of armoured warfare. Others might be seen as more specifi-

108   The A10 bridgelayer backing away from its bridge provides a clear view of the special gearbox and lifting arms as well as the hull machine-gun which was unique to this version.

109   The prototype Covenanter scissors bridgelayer during trials at EBE Christchurch.

cally related to tanks but one, at least, was quite bizarre under any circumstances. This was the idea that one could dazzle one's opponents into submission. It should be understood that, early in the war in particular, the very idea of night-time operations, especially where tanks were involved, was looked upon with something approaching horror by most professional soldiers. There were examples of regiments that had been carefully trained to fight in the dark but the majority saw it only as a recipe for confusion. Even so it was clear that any army which could master the technique would be a force to be reckoned with and any scheme which might achieve it was bound to be seized upon.

The idea had first been suggested during the Great War by a naval officer, Commander de Thoren, but it came to nothing. Between the wars de Thoren teamed up with a Greek engineer, Marcel Mitzakis, a naturalised Briton who had developed a sort of armoured searchlight. The syndicate was financed by the Duke of Westminster and backed by General J F C Fuller, who was appointed tactical advisor, but the War Office showed very little interest and allowed Mitzakis to offer it to the French. They appear not to have appreciated it either, and it was not until June 1940 that the British Army witnessed a trial at Lulworth which apparently went so well that immediate orders were placed. The scheme depended on the principle that a man could be temporarily blinded if a bright light was shone in his face. It was further discovered that if the light flickered the effect was even more pronounced, because the victim's pupils would rapidly dilate and contract in an effort to counteract the alternating effects of bright light and darkness. The flickering coincided conveniently with the need to protect the light source from hostile fire, and a rapidly moving armoured shutter was developed which only unmasked the beam for split seconds at a time. Tanks equipped with these lights could be used in night attacks to dazzle enemy strongpoints – pillboxes, for instance, which their own infantry could clearly see. Two searchlight tanks would station themselves some yards apart with their lights focused on the objective. The defenders could only fire blindly while in the triangle of darkness formed between the two tanks and their target, assault troops would move in for the kill.

In theory it sounded fine, and following a period of intensive research orders were placed for 300 bullet-proof turrets (250 of which would be manufactured in the USA) and ten cast-iron training turrets, designed to fit the Matilda. They were tall, upright structures with a vertical searchlight slit, Besa machine-gun and dummy 2-pounder barrel to disguise their true purpose. Around the top of the turret was a series of cooling louvres while inside it was divided into two compartments. On the left sat the operator, who could fire the machine gun but whose main duty was to change the carbon elements when they burned out in the arc lamp. For this unenviable duty he was provided with a pair of asbestos gloves. The arc lamp was housed in the righthand compartment, shining its light into a large parabolic mirror that reflected the beam through the slit. An extra dynamo, driven off the tank's engines, operated the light.

The first regiment to convert to the new weapon was 11th RTR which in June 1942 was sent out to Egypt. Possibly this was because there was plenty of room in the desert to conduct secret field trials, but bearing in mind the desperate situation out there, the choice of codename for the device may be more significant; it was called the Canal Defence Light (CDL). The modification to Matilda involved little more than a change of turret, so a special portable crane was developed to fit this type of tank and quickly effect the change on a fellow machine. Great things were expected of it and security was almost stifling but in the period under review none were ever used in action, despite the fact that by the end of 1942 five RAC regiments had converted to the role.

One thing the British Army learned in France was a healthy respect for German air power, particularly the dive-bombing Stuka, and this focused attention on the need for some form of mobile anti-aircraft defence to work with tanks and transport columns which, in effect, meant anti-aircraft tanks. It led to a rash of proposals, some of a highly dubious nature, and to the involvement of a very strange RTR officer, Major T A Lakeman MBE, whose inventive genius was only matched by his inordinate skill in annoying people. The first result of the experience in France was approval for the fitting of AA Bren guns to ordinary service tanks, on the scale of one weapon to every three tanks, but other developments were in hand. As early as 1939 the Gunnery School at Lulworth was working on designs based on the Light Tank Mark V. One was adapted to carry a pair of 15mm Besa guns in an open mounting which, by all accounts, worked very well. These weapons, however, were in very short supply and no more could be spared for this purpose so the prototype remained at Lulworth, stationed outside the guardroom at the main entrance to drive off enemy aircraft. The next model, on the same type of chassis, carried a quadruple Browning machine-gun turret of the type normally fitted to the Boulton and Paul Defiant. The guns worked perfectly well but the perspex cover proved to be more of a nuisance than it was worth and, after some modification, was removed, leaving the guns exposed. Folding steel plates were now fitted all around the mounting which folded flat for firing. Ammunition-feed problems with the Brownings then encouraged the designers to look at the 7.92mm Besa instead, but by this time the Department of Tank Design had become involved and the experiments were placed on a more official footing.

Meanwhile Major Lakeman had great hopes for the Bren gun. He developed a whole range of spring-assisted mountings, for use in trucks or from the ground, as rivals to the similar Motley system. Most of these worked on the same principle as the anglepoise desk lamp, in that

110 *The Lulworth designed anti-aircraft tank mounting twin 15mm Besa guns on a Light Mark V chassis.*

111 *Another Light Mark V mounting four Brownings. This picture shows the tank in its second form when the perspex aircraft turret had been replaced by folding side panels.*

strong springs were used to counteract the weight of the guns and in extreme cases enabled one man to control and fire up to four Bren-guns at a time. Lakeman than adapted his system by adding a sort of armoured hood which one observer likened to the body of a hansom cab, and versions were developed to fit onto the Loyd Carrier and a 15-cwt truck. Similar mountings were prepared by Vauxhall Motors in conjunction with the DTD (who Lakeman accused of stealing his ideas), and these were also tested in lightly armoured Bedford trucks. A wooden mock-up was even prepared for a fully armoured Loyd carrier with a narrow streamlined hull mounting a small turret, but it was cancelled because of its weight before an armoured version could be built. A Universal Carrier was also modified by covering over the front compartment and fitting a small turret over the gunner's seat, and this mounted two Bren guns, but the problem in every case was the weapon itself. The Bren was simply not capable of sustained fire on this scale; it could not be modified to accept belt feed, and in any case it was prone to overheating when it fired long bursts.

General Macready and General Pope were strong advocates of the AA tank, but both men realised that with the situation as it stood in 1940 there was neither time nor resources to develop special vehicles for the work, and conversions to existing light tanks appeared to be the most sensible alternative. Major W A Turner, the Experimental Officer at Lulworth, played an important part in the development work and also proposed that such tanks should also be capable of engaging ground targets. His ideas were approved by the War Office in January 1941. They saw such tanks as a valuable adjunct to the beach defences in the event of invasion, and in the wider context saw their role as 'giving immediate protection to tanks in contact with the enemy, protecting headquarters formations and as a possible deterrent against aircraft attacking "B" vehicle columns'. Obviously in this last case a wheeled mount would be more suitable and Turner

112 *The strange Loyd Carrier based anti-aircraft vehicle in the mock-up state which was as far as it got.*

emphasised that his turret was designed to fit both light tanks and armoured cars. Production began later in the year, the first model being the Light AA Tank Mark I, based on the Light Mark VIA. It had a raised superstructure on the hull, supporting a special turret mounting four Besa-guns abreast. They were issued on a scale of four to each HQ Squadron of an armoured regiment as they became available, but production was slow due to other priorities. A Mark II version soon appeared, usually mounted on the Light Mark VIB hull. It had a lower superstructure but a higher, less cramped turret with improved sighting arrangements. Sixty were built of both marks at an estimated cost of £250 per conversion. A further fifty turrets of similar pattern to the Mark II were also supplied for armoured cars but it seems unlikely that many were converted. The chosen chassis was that of the Humber Mark I armoured car. Light AA tanks served with the Royal Armoured Corps in the Western Desert but no reports have been traced to illustrate their effectiveness.

113 *The crew of a Boys anti-tank rifle take on a Light AA tank Mark I at point blank range during an exercise in Southern England.*

114 *Based on a Humber armoured car this vehicle mounts the same type of turret as fitted to the light AA tank Mark II.*

The flamethrower is a terrifying weapon but once it is combined with the power and mobility of an armoured vehicle it becomes positively awesome. There often appear to be moral objections to it in peacetime which are only overcome by the pressures of war. It existed in the First World War and was even considered for fitting in tanks, but for the next twenty years it virtually disappeared from the military scene. In 1939 it came up for consideration again, originally as a man-portable weapon of very short range, but during the emergency period of 1940/41 it was revived in mobile form as a defensive measure. The great advantage of such a mounting is that it can also bear the weight of a powerful pump, which increases the range of the flame jet dramatically when compared with the lightweight system that an individual soldier can carry. The new development was signalised by the formation, shortly after Dunkirk, of the Petroleum Warfare Department under General Sir Donald Banks, as he later became.

There was a fear in some quarters that the use of ordinary petrol in large mechanical pumps would prove as much a danger to the user as his victim since a blowback could ignite the reservoir from which the fuel was drawn. In an attempt to overcome this difficulty R P Fraser of London University worked on the development of a thickened fuel which was expected to behave more sensibly. In order to test it out an ordinary Commer lorry was armoured and fitted with a special turret with an annular type of dual nozzle projector. The work was carried out by the Lagonda Car Company of Feltham. Parallel with this the chief engineer of the AEC company, G J Rackham – who played an important part in the development of the early tanks – produced what was known as the Heavy Pump Unit. It was based on a suitably armoured version of the AEC six-wheel drive heavy lorry. As its name implies it was a massive affair with two projectors. The main one, driven by a fire-engine pump, was located inside the body. It was capable of both ground and anti-aircraft fire although in the latter role its maximum range was limited to 300 feet. The other projector was smaller, fitted to a two-wheeled carriage and stowed externally on the back of the vehicle. From here it could be dismounted and pushed a short distance from the parent vehicle, to which it was connected by a flexible pipe, while the operator sheltered behind a small shield. Although earmarked for coastal defence it was never actually taken into service although it gave some spectacular demonstrations.

The same chassis was used as the basis for the Heavy Cockatrice. This was the next development by Fraser and the Lagonda company along with a smaller version on the Bedford QL four-wheel drive chassis. Both types had weird, non-symmetrical armoured hulls with tiny flame-projector turrets. Six of the former were built and issued to the RAF for airfield defence, while the smaller Bedford Cockatrice, of which sixty were built, performed a similar duty at Royal Naval Air Stations for the Fleet Air Arm. Rackham and AEC went on to build the Basilisk on an AEC Matador chassis. The hull was similar to the AEC armoured car with a built-in pump unit and a small turret to house the flame-projector, but it never got beyond the prototype stage.

As the emphasis moved away from defence towards attack the flamethrower was now examined as a potential assault weapon. For this purpose a tracked chassis would clearly be more suitable and at first the Universal Carrier was considered. A prototype was constructed in October 1940 to a design worked out by Mr S W Adey and Lieutenant Colonel Martin, commanding the 47th (London) Division. Their brainchild was nicknamed the Adey-Martin drainpipe because the tube, leading from the fuel tank to the projector, ran along the side of the vehicle's hull. Official reaction was initially unfavourable, but following a series of demonstrations it was taken up with enthusiasm by the Canadians who sought help from Lagonda. Their model also featured an external feed-pipe

115　The AEC Heavy Pump Unit fills the air with smoke and flame at a War Office demonstration.

116　A similar event on Salisbury Plain features two of the Heavy Cockatrice vehicles and the AEC Basilisk.

117　The smaller Bedford Cockatrice was based on the four-wheel drive QL chassis.

drawing fuel from a pair of cylindrical tanks at the back, but its limited range, of only forty feet, did not appeal to the War Office, so after a few had been built production was switched to Canada. It was known, unofficially at first, by the codename Ronson.

The British now began to concentrate on tank-based flamethrowers and two types were developed under the auspices of the PWD and the Ministry of Supply. The former was developed by Rackham and AEC and was fitted to a Valentine. It was a cumbersome affair based on the Heavy Pump Unit with the big projector mounted on the front offside trackguard. Fuel was carried in a large cylindrical tank in a two-wheeled trailer while pressure was provided by gas from cylinders of the type used to inflate barrage balloons. The Ministry version looked altogether more professional. Once again a Valentine served as the trials vehicle and the projector was mounted in a small turret which, like the PWD version, was fitted on the right trackguard. The fuel trailer in this case was smaller, and armoured, being basically box-shaped and running on two wheels. The propellant was created by slow-burning cordite which proved incapable of building up pressure quickly enough, so the projector was unable to fire long bursts, or even short ones in quick succession. After each brief squirt it needed a ten-second rest to build up pressure again, and at a comparative trial on Hangmoor Ranges in March 1942 the PWD model was selected and the two research teams merged.

Meanwhile Rackham had proceeded with experiments of his own. One concept, based on the carrier, resulted ultimately in the Wasp, which will be discussed in the sequel to this book. Lagonda worked on a suggestion put forward by a Major Oke that the normal jettison fuel container, fitted to most tanks at this time, would make an ideal reservoir for a flamethrower instead of the awkward trailer. This was connected up to a Wasp-type projector and fitted to a Churchill tank where it was operated by a crew member in the hull machine-gunner's seat. With strong backing from Lord Mountbatten, Chief of Combined Operations, the work was pushed ahead without reference to the Department of Tank Design and was ready for operational use within three months. It would be the first type of British-designed tank flamethrower to take part in an operation, as described later.

Although it is not classed as specialised armour in the normal sense the Armoured Recovery Vehicle (ARV), being based on a tank chassis, cannot pass without mention. Its development is covered in detail by a companion volume in this series*. The ARV is now such an indispensable part of the military scene that it is difficult to realise that when the war began nothing like it existed in the British Army. Odd prototypes had appeared before the war but the need for them on a large scale had simply

*B S Baxter, *Breakdown: a history of recovery vehicles in the British Army*, HMSO, 1989.

118 The flamethrower designed by the Ministry of Supply and mounted on a Valentine is put through its paces.

not been appreciated. As with bridgelayers the accepted practice in Britain, when design work began early in 1942, was to base the recovery vehicle on the same type of chassis as the tanks they were intended to recover. Three models were developed initially using Covenanter, Crusader and Churchill hulls, but the first two were soon rejected as unsuitable and the Churchill was the first type to enter service. All three were basically turretless tanks equipped with light lifting-jibs and various items of ancillary equipment for undertaking field maintenance. If they could not repair a tank in situ then they towed it off the battlefield to where it could be dealt with. The main problem was the lack of a built-in winch which prevented the ARV from hauling a tank out of any situation where it could not get close enough to tow. Some Churchill ARVs served with REME units in Tunisia and they remained in service until the end of the war, although better models appeared later. When the Grant and later the Sherman came into service, some of these were adapted as ARVs in the same way and all of these turretless versions were classed as ARV Mark I models of whatever tanks they were based upon.

Alongside the mainstream development of specialised armour, if there was such a thing, there soon appeared a whole range of others, most of which were just as quickly abandoned. They range from the ingenious to the mildly crazy although most displayed a bit of both. A few of the more interesting ones that appeared before the end of 1942 are covered briefly here. One of the simplest, based on a Matilda, was a means of destroying barbed-wire entanglements by firing an explosive tube, known as a Bangalore torpedo, into them. The tube was fitted in a bracket on the left side of the tank and carried rather as a medieval knight would wield his lance. When it approached the wire the tube was elevated and fired into the wire where it could be detonated by remote control. Prewar experiments with wireless-controlled tanks continued during the war and resulted in Black Prince, the codename

119 A rear view of the Churchill Oke flamethrower showing the fuel reservoir and feed pipe leading to the front mounted projector.

120 The Matilda modified to carry and launch a Bangalore torpedo for clearing wire entanglements.

for a remote-controlled Matilda. Most of the technical problems were overcome so that the crewless tank could be driven about, but the scheme was handicapped by the short range at which the equipment worked and by the need to have the operator always close enough to the vehicle to see what it was doing.

The problem of crossing wide trenches had been solved during the First World War by the fascine, a large bundle of sticks carried on top of the tank and launched into the offending trench. Before this was reinvented, later in the war, another novel solution was tried. This took the form of a standard industrial cable drum which was pushed ahead of the tank and detached when it fell into the trench. The main difficulty in this case seems to have been the width of the drum and the weight it could bear. Another Great War idea revived was a short, wedge-shaped ramp, mounted in this case on a short set of tracks, which could be pushed by a tank and placed against an obstacle to assist the tank in climbing over it. Before Sir Donald Bailey developed his famous prefabricated bridge the army relied on the tubular steel Inglis type which dated from the First World War. At Christchurch in 1919 one of

these had been mounted on tracks and pushed over a gap by a tank. This idea was also resurrected in 1941 and tested with a Matilda as the propelling vehicle. None of the equipment mentioned above was ever used on active service, either because it proved impractical or because the opportunity simply did not arise, but the bridge-pushing concept was later adapted on a much bigger scale to suit the Bailey Bridge, and at least two of the other ideas enjoyed further brief flurries of interest in slightly different forms, but these will be recounted in the sequel.

As already described, some early versions of the Universal Carrier were supplied as observation post vehicles for the Royal Artillery. This idea was also expanded later to involve the use of tanks which, if nothing else, provided the forward observation officer with a good deal more protection while he carried out his dangerous work. Some Crusaders were modified for this task and may be taken as typical. The turret was gutted, although this fact was disguised by the addition of a dummy gun-barrel fitted to the outside. Obviously no ammunition was carried so the interior was fitted out with extra wireless sets, plotting boards and other equipment, while the turret itself was locked in one position. Looking more or less like any other tank the OP Crusader could advance in the midst of a fighting troop while remaining in direct touch with artillery batteries in the rear. Yet another simple idea which had its origins in the First World War was the Bobbin. This was the unambiguous codename for a stout roll of hessian, or canvas matting, wrapped around a drum and carried at the front of a tank. When it approached a suspect patch of soft or boggy ground the matting was unwound beneath the tracks and left in place to support following vehicles. It was only used operationally on the Churchill and the first version, which appeared in 1942, actually used two narrow rolls of material, one ahead of each track, rather than the full-width type adopted later. It was also tested, on a smaller scale, with the Universal Carrier.

Although they are slowly disappearing one can still find, dotted about the country, firmly rooted blocks of concrete which were emplaced at vulnerable sites to prevent enemy tanks from getting through in the invasion scare period

121 The original TLC carpet laying device fitted to a Churchill II.

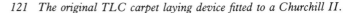

of 1940. Other less permanent ideas were also tried, and these are interesting only to the extent that British tanks were then used to test their effectiveness. They ranged from stout steel-girder structures to huge tangles of scaffolding and even old railway wagonwheels which were simply scattered about the fields. Most of them appear to have been developed by an organisation known as the Anti-Tank Experimental Establishment which, in time, became parent to another body, the Obstacle Assault Centre.

Waterways have always posed a serious problem to tanks. As we have already seen, various bridging expedients were developed to deal with narrower ones but there were always lakes, estuaries and wider rivers to be considered, along with the problems likely to be experienced when tanks are landed on an open beach from the sea. Amphibious tanks seem an obvious solution but they present all manner of conflicting problems. Generally it can be said that if such machines are made light enough to float on their own account they will also be extremely vulnerable even to light anti-tank weapons. On the other hand if they are well enough armoured it is very difficult to make them float. In 1938 Vickers-Armstrong built a light amphibious tank to General Staff specification L4E1. It was a two-man machine, powered by a Meadows engine which drove the tracks on land or twin propellors in the water. The armoured hull was very narrow, and fitted

with a small machine-gun turret, but on each side were kapok-filled alloy flotation-chambers which gave the machine a boat-like appearance. Steel was later used to replace the alloy but the tank still looked the same and on test in 1939 it was reported to have performed very well. However it was noted that the area of river bank where it came ashore had to be chosen with great care. Thick reeds and soft mud had to be avoided since either would trap the tank in such a way that it neither had enough buoyancy for the propellors to move it, nor sufficient grip for the tracks to bite. A much larger model was built to the design of the Department of Naval Land Equipment, parent of the abortive Nellie project. Three variants were built by the engineering firm Braithwaites of Newport, Monmouthshire and classified as AT1★, AT1★★ and AT1★★★ (AT, of course, for Amphibious Tank). Mechanically they were based on the Covenanter with the same kind of turret, but the hull was large and deep, with a very high track-profile to provide sufficient buoyancy. Special track shoes, incorporating flanges that acted as paddles, were fitted to move the tank through the water and, although all three models were of similar appearance, the first type had no sprung suspension while the other two did. Following trials in and around Barry Docks examples of each type went down to Farnborough for evaluation and, much later in the war, came back to South Wales to be scrapped by Curran Brothers of Cardiff.

122 The Vickers-Armstrong light amphibious tank L4E1 in brand new condition. The cowl that surrounds the starboard propellor can be seen at the back while the shaft that drives it is visible, running from the front sprocket and behind the return rollers. The ribbed panels form the kapok filled flotation chambers.

123 *The massive AT1* amphibious tank gives a trench crossing demonstration on the beach at Barry Island in South Wales. The Covenanter turret is dwarfed by the deep hull.*

The idea that a tank could cross a river simply by driving across the bottom had been pioneered by the Russians even before the war, probably because they lacked the good stone bridges found in Europe, and it was later taken up by the Germans, no doubt for exactly the same reason, but also in connection with the projected invasion of Britain. During the war it was also tried once by the British. The work was carried out at EBE Christchurch in 1940, the test vehicle being the redundant prototype cruiser A9E1 – although, if it proved successful, the plan was to adapt it to the Matilda. From a purely practical point of view A9E1 was not a very good choice. Being a prototype it was of bolted construction and over 100 bolts were missing when it arrived at Christchurch which had to be replaced before any experimental work could begin. Also it had three turrets, all of which required sealing, and all the weapons were missing so the apertures needed plating over. On the other hand, because it presented the trials team with just about every problem imaginable, it provided useful experience. Early tests in three or four feet of water revealed a succession of leaks that were gradually made good until the small bilge pump which had been installed was capable of keeping pace with the slight ingress. Unfortunately the tank also showed a curious propensity to float, especially at the front end, so three tons of pig-iron was distributed in the forward turrets and beneath a false floor in the main one. The original air inlet and outlet louvres were fitted with hydraulically operated flaps and the cooling fan was screened to prevent it from spraying the engine and electrical components with water. Air for the engine was drawn down a concentric tube some 20 feet high, which led into the engine compartment; fresh air passed down the outer tube while exhausted air was returned up the central one. Exhaust fumes were carried up another pipe attached to the outside of this column. The crew, which consisted of one army officer and two civilians, was trained in the use of Davis submarine escape apparatus, suitably modified for wearing in tanks by Siebe-Gorman Ltd. Wearing this equipment they were able to survey the river bed at the crossing point on foot, and this helped them to gain confidence in its effectiveness. Finally all joints and hatch covers were sealed with a Bostik compound while rubber ribbon was used on the turret rings so that they could still be traversed without destroying the seal, although there was no intention of doing this under water.

124 *The submersible A9 cruiser at Christchurch with its breather pipe erected.*

125 *A Light Tank Mark VI, equipped with Straussler Series 2 floats, takes a dip among the lilies on Mytchett Lake near Aldershot.*

126 *The swimming Crusader with floats attached and the Atherton Jack rigged before it takes the plunge in Langstone Harbour. The special scoop shaped tracks were fitted to drive the tank through the water.*

The official trial was carried out on 24 May 1940. The Stour was crossed successfully in ten feet of water without mishap. The driver, of course, was totally blind under water so a tall periscope was fitted to the turret to enable the commander to pass instructions to him. In practice even this did not work very well so a telephone line was installed and the tank conned from the riverbank. As an added precaution a towrope was connected and slung from the top of the pillar, but in the last resort the crew would be able to flood the tank and escape, using their breathing apparatus. Fortunately these precautions proved unnecessary although the experiment was terminated. The War Office stated that it had no plans to build special submersible tanks and felt that the work required to modify service types was more trouble than it was worth. In later years the technique has been adopted by most NATO and Eastern Bloc armies, but a good deal of credit is still due to the three brave men who pioneered it.

Before the war, in Hungary, Nicholas Straussler had built a series of unconventional light tanks which could swim with the aid of special floats and when he came to Britain the idea was extended to suit a Vickers light tank. It was unwieldy but it worked, and solved the difficulty of getting tanks across waterways without sacrificing armour protection or fighting ability. The Series 2 floats, designed for the Light Tank Mark VI, entered production and 120 sets were made and issued to Divisional Cavalry Regiments on a scale of six sets per unit, but they were never used operationally, presumably because the requirement never arose. Series 3 floats were also developed for cruiser tanks and tested on a Crusader in Langstone Harbour near Portsmouth. Unlike the light tanks, which relied solely on their ordinary tracks to propel them through the water, the Crusader had special scoop-shaped trackshoes to help it along. Being a lot larger these floats needed more men and quite a lot of effort to fit, and a special turret attachment, the Atherton Jack, was provided to support them. This was a standard item which clamped to the turret and could be used to lift out components like final drive gearboxes during field maintenance. The tank performed quite well on inland waters and even a calm sea but it had more than enough drawbacks. In addition to the problems of transporting and fitting the floats they could not be used for a beach landing since they made the tank too wide to pass through the bows of a landing craft. Since this was a major requirement they too were abandoned.

Yet it was Straussler who ultimately solved the problem. Discarding the float idea he took an entirely original approach and surrounded the hull of a tank with a collapsible, rubberised canvas screen which, in effect, converted the tank into a large open boat. The screen was raised with the help of air-filled rubber tubes and then locked in place by tubular steel struts which kept it rigid and in shape. The vehicle could then drive into the water, from a landing craft or river bank, swim across the wet gap and drive out on the other side where the screen was automatically collapsed. At a stroke the tank was ready for action, the gun unmasked and the turret free to swing. Straussler was well aware that power from the tracks alone would not be sufficient to drive the tank in a seaway so he fitted a power take-off to the transmission which led to a small propellor. It was this optional means of propulsion, tracks or screw, which was reflected in its official title, Duplex Drive (DD).

The experiment was first conducted on a Tetrarch light tank which swam, initially, in June 1941 on the Welsh Harp reservoir at Hendon and later at the War Office training establishment on Hayling Island. Among the firms involved in the work was the famous PB Cow Company, makers of the Lilo airbed. DD tanks were seen as the perfect solution to the problem of landing tanks on a hostile beach, something that British planners had been considering since Dunkirk. An important feature of the DD concept was that it could be applied to virtually any tank, as long as the flotation screen was made deep enough to give adequate displacement, and the first type chosen for production was the Valentine. Contracts were issued in the summer of 1942 for the conversion of 450 tanks by the Metropolitan-Cammell Carriage and Wagon Company in Birmingham.

This is not the place to attempt a history of landing craft, but since the immediate future of British tank warfare was so bound up with them a brief outline is essential. As usual it is possible to trace their origins back to the earliest days of organised warfare but development of the mechanical, self-propelled type really belongs to the inter-war years. At first it was confined to a small band of enthusiasts working on the fringe of military and naval interest, who developed a series of small vessels capable of carrying one 16-ton tank which was landed across a bow ramp, a sort of drawbridge, directly on to the beach. Work began in earnest after the fall of France and resulted in two basic tank-carrying types. Mechanised Landing Craft (MLCs, later LCMs) were small ship-to-shore vessels capable of handling one tank, while Tank Landing Craft (LCTs) could carry four or five and make cross-Channel trips fully laden.

The smaller craft were used initially for raiding, carrying troops and light equipment instead of tanks, and some took part in the Norwegian campaign, while the larger types were used to ferry tanks into Tobruk during the siege. A plan has already been mentioned to effect a major landing on the North African coast to outflank Rommel but this was never launched. Thus it was that the first time tanks were landed during an offensive operation was, indirectly against a new enemy, the Japanese, although the immediate target was a French garrison. The operation was mounted against the Vichy French island of Madagascar with the objective of securing it against a potential Japanese invasion that could pose a threat to Allied positions in East Africa. The key to success was the city of

Diego Suarez and its harbour, Antsirane. Once that was taken the rest of the island should present no problem. The action took place over three days, 5 to 7 May 1942. Six Tetrarchs and six Valentines of B Special Service Squadron RAC took part in the main assault which bore the brunt of French resistance, but the opposition collapsed when fifty Royal Marines landed directly inside the naval base from the destroyer *HMS Anthony*. It was a model of inter-service combined operations which augured well for the future. After the tanks were withdrawn a number of Marmon-Herrington armoured cars were used by the Allied troops to reduce small pockets of resistance and keep the peace.

Meanwhile, in Britain, an amphibious training centre had been established at Inverary, on Loch Fyne, where training could be carried out using the larger types of landing craft. Another was set up at Westward Ho! in North Devon which became known as the Combined Operations Experimental Establishment (COXE) where waterproofing, and what became known as deep-wading techniques, were developed. How much this derived from the earlier experiments with the cruiser A9E1 at Christchurch is not clear, but it would be typical of the British approach if the people at COXE knew nothing about these at all. In any case deep wading is not total immersion, it is simply a means of conferring on a vehicle the ability to operate for a short time in between three and six feet of water. This involves sealing all vulnerable apertures, or masking certain vital components, and adding extended exhaust pipes and air-intake trunking up to the height, in a tank at least, of the turret ring. As it was perfected it was applied to a great variety of vehicles and special booklets were printed showing exactly how it should be done. The extension trunking was also standardised for each type of vehicle and manufactured so that it could be supplied as a 'Pack Flat' kit ready to be fitted when the need arose by trained unit fitters.

Since it forms the subject of the final part of this chapter the Churchill tank can be looked at in more detail in this context. The first stage was to seal all openings, hull doors, engine hatches and other hinged panels with various mastic compounds and tapes. Waterproof covers would then be placed over the weapons to completely seal all openings while the engine itself was treated with similar substances to coat the spark plugs, magneto and other electrical parts. The turret ring was given the same kind of protection although here, since it was vital to have the tank operational in the shortest possible time, Cordex explosive charges were incorporated with the seals which could blow them off in seconds. Lightweight steel trunking was then fitted over the main air louvres at the sides while extension exhaust pipes, leading upwards, were also added. Because of their increased draught most larger landing craft would ground some yards from the water's edge and, when the ramp went down, the tanks would have to negotiate fairly deep water, possibly aggravated by waves, for a short distance. Thus the need for effective deep-wading gear was vital to the success of a landing.

Enough has already been written about the Anglo-Canadian landings at Deippe, in August 1942, to overlook the wider issues and concentrate upon the performance of the tanks. They were all Churchills, manned exclusively by Canadians of the Calgary Regiment (14th Canadian Army Tank Battalion) and they included Marks I, II and III; the latter of course armed with 6-pounders. Three were equipped with Oke flamethrowers while three more carried a Beach Tracklaying Device, the original Canadian designed version of Bobbin, to assist the tanks over the shingle beach. Some Daimler scout cars and carriers, one of them a Loyd, also took part.

Twenty-nine of the Regiment's tanks, all fitted with deep-wading gear, left their landing craft but only about half that number managed to get across the sea wall. All the flamethrowers were disabled before they could get into action although it proved possible to make some limited use of the carpet layers. For a long time afterwards it was believed that many tanks failed to leave the beach because shingle worked its way into the tracks and caused them

to break, but it now appears that most of this damage was due to anti-tank fire. This was also responsible for jamming some turrets but it is also clear that there were very few instances of the armour being penetrated. Even where they did manage to climb onto the esplanade tanks were unable to penetrate very much further, and when the attack collapsed it proved impossible to re-embark any of them.

One can question the wisdom of committing a new type of tank to an operation where, it seems obvious, some would fall into enemy hands, but the optimistic planners had never reckoned on losing all of them. In any case each tank was supposed to be equipped with a demolition device which, in the event, was rarely used because even disabled tanks were being used as shelters from the intense fire by weary and wounded men. Those that fell into German hands were soon evaluated but they failed to impress their captors. Criticism was levelled at the entire design from armour layout to track configuration, while the guns were discounted in the light of what the Germans were now encountering on the Eastern Front. The performance too was scorned although according to one

127 *Disaster at Dieppe. A Canadian soldiers tends to his wounded comrades in the lee of a wrecked Churchill while two German sentries stand by and a Landing Craft burns in the background. Although most of the deep wading gear has been jettisoned or shot away one can still see the extended exhaust pipes behind the turret.*

report German technical experts were able to effect an improvement that the British designers had apparently never thought of. As designed, the top run of the track on a Churchill ran along skid-rails, but the Germans experimented by fitting inverted suspension units from damaged tanks as return rollers, and this modest alteration made them much freer running.

As the last survivors made their way back across the Channel the Germans emerged to pick their way among the smoking wrecks and twisted bodies that littered the beach. They wondered at the purpose of the attack and at the archaic-looking British tanks. One thing they could not know, that within two years the Allies would be back in overwhelming strength, and with them would be more Churchills, cured of all their present ills and more than capable of fighting right through to the end. But that is another story.

Index

Burgin, Dr Leslie 4
Burton, Geoffrey 4, 66, 88, 91

Cairo 71, 109, 113
Calais 27
Campbell, Sir Malcolm 36
Canadian Pacific Railway 94
Canal Defence Light 126
Cappuzzo 71, 79, 80, 81
Carden, Sir John 1, 7, 8, 29, 43, 47
Carden-Loyd 42, 47, 71
Carr, L. E. 88, 92, 94
Caterpillar D8 tractor 103, 125
'Cauldron' 109
Chamberlain, A. 101
Cherbourg 27
Chobry, S. S. 28
Christie, J. Walter 91
Chullora, N. S. W. 103
Churchill, Winston 1, 4, 26, 43, 58, 77,
    88, 93, 111, 113
Clarke, General Sir Campbell 18
Cleare, G. V. 58
Clearwater, Florida 91
Combined Operations Experimental
    Establishment (COXE) 135
Concrete Ltd. 36
Coulter Plough 120, 121
County Commercial Cars 46
Cow, P. B. & Co. 135
Coward, Noel 90
Crabtree, A. W. & Co. 11
Crawford, Major General 67, 68
Crete 77
'Crusader' 81, 82, 107
Crüwell, General Ludwig 49, 82
Curran Bros. 123, 132
Cyprus 77

David Brown Ltd. 4
Department of Tank Design 4, 42, 48,
    58, 67, 104, 122, 130
Derna 76
De Thoren, Commander Oliver 126
Dewar, Michael 87, 88, 90, 91, 93
D'Eyncourt, Sir Eustace Tennyson 22,
    25
Dieppe 136
Director of Artillery 64
Disston Tractor Co. 103
Dominion Bridge Co. 96
Duncan, Sir Andrew 4, 67
Dunkirk 27, 62, 128
Durrant, A. A. M. 4, 65
Du Toit, Major A. S. J. 122

Elles, Sir Hugh 43
El Mechili 74, 79
Empire Song, M. V. 79
English Electric Co. 22, 62
Eritrea 77, 104
Experimental Armoured Force 25
Experimental Bridging Establishment
    (EBE) 6, 119, 123, 124, 133

Ferguson, Harry 120
Foote VC, Lt-Col. H. R. B. 110

Ford (Canada) 97
Fraser, Professor R. P. 128
Fuller, J. F. C. 6, 126
Gallabat 120
Galpin, Captain S. G. 124
Gazala 93, 108, 109, 110
General Staff 4, 22, 42, 43, 48, 49, 60,
    62, 64, 120, 132
Gibraltar 77
Glubb, Colonel J. B. 105
Goodall, Sir Stanley 25
Gott, Lt-Gen. W. H. E. 113
Greece 77
Guy Motors 16, 40, 46, 47

Hafia Ridge 80
Halfaya Pass 75, 79, 80, 81
Hamilton Bridge Co. 95
Hangmoor Ranges 130
Harland & Wolff 5, 8, 21
Henry Meadows Ltd. 22, 42
Hitler, Adolf 23, 70, 78, 113, 116
Hobart, Maj-Gen. P. C. S. 70, 71, 73, 74
Hopkins, L. J. W. 25
Hore-Belisha, Leslie 4
Hotchkiss et Cie 18, 88
Humber Ltd. 47
Hutt Valley 103

International Harvester Corp. 95
Inverary 135
Iraq 77

Jerram, Lt-Col. R. M. 75
Johannesburg 98
John Fowler & Co. 5, 120, 121

Karrier Motors 16, 40, 47
Kenya 70, 105
King George VI 3, 38, 69
Knightsbridge 109, 110, 112
Knott, Lieutenant 90
Korean War 101

Lagonda Car Co. 128
Lakeman, Major T. A. 126, 127
Lakenheath 69
Landing Craft Mechanised (LCM) 135
Landing Craft Tank (LCT) 135
Landships Committee 21
Langstone Harbour 134
Lawrence, T. E. 71
Leese, Lt-Gen. Sir Oliver 113
Lend Lease 66, 92, 93
Leyland Motors 13, 36, 62, 67
Lima Locomotive Works 90, 93
Lithgow, Sir James 4, 24
Little, Leslie 20
London Midland & Scottish Railway 13,
    17, 36, 60, 62
London Transport 4
Lothian, Lord 88
Loyd, Captain Vivian 42
Lucas, Oliver 66, 67
Lulworth Camp (Gunnery School) 40,
    63, 65, 126, 127
Lumsden, Lt-Gen. Herbert 108

Macleod Ross, Brigadier G. 18
Macready, General 4, 66, 127
Madagascar 135
Maginot Line 20, 25, 26
Malta 77, 79
Margesson, Captain 66
Marmon-Herrington Co. 97, 98, 100,
    105
Marshall, General G. C. 93
Martel, General G. le Q. 47, 123
Martin, Lt-Col. 128
Maskelyene, Major Jasper 79
Master General of Ordnance 4
Mavor, Colonel William 94
Mechnisation Board 20, 101
Mechanisation Experimental
    Establishment 4, 18, 46
Mechanisation Experimental
    Establishment (ME) 112
Mersah Matruh 71, 72, 74, 79, 110
Merritt, Dr. H. E. 4, 21
Merritt-Brown 22, 58
Merz, C. H. 22
Merz & McLellan 22
Messervey, Maj-Gen. F. W. 108
Metro-Cammell 42, 135
Micklem, Commander Sir Robert 42, 69
Ministry of Aircraft Production 66
Ministry (Minister) of Supply 21, 66, 67
Mitzakis, Marcel 126
Montgomery, General Sir Bernard 113,
    114, 115, 116
Montreal 94
Montreal Locomotive Works 94
Morris, William see Lord Nuffield
Morris, Lieutenant W. A. 38
Morris-Commerical Cars 5, 16, 18, 45,
    46, 47
Morrison, Herbert 4, 88
Mountbatten, Lord Louis 130
Msus 108
Mussolini, Benito 70, 71
Narvik 28
Neame, Lt-Gen. Sir Philip 78
Nellie 25, 26, 132
Neutrality Act 87
Newcastle, HMS 86
New York 88, 89
Norrie, Lt-Gen. C. W. N. 108
Norris, Major 116
Norway 28
Nuffield, Lord 5, 62, 67
Nuffield Mechanisation & Aero 5, 7, 11,
    13, 17, 57, 63, 65, 86

Obstacle Assault Centre (OAC) 132
O'Connor, Lt-Gen. Sir Richard 78
Oke, Major 130, 136
Ontario 95, 97
Ordnance Board (USA) 89, 92, 94
Ottawa 94

Pakenham Walsh, Maj-Gen. 89, 94
Palestine 70, 105
Paris 28
Patton, General George S. 93
Perrier, R. 101

Printed in the United Kingdom for HMSO.
Dd.294476, 11/93, C10, 3397/5, 5673, 264716.